D1593748

Hermit

THE MYSTERIOUS LIFE OF JIM WHYTE

JEFFREY H. RYAN

Other books by Jeffrey H. Ryan

Appalachian Odyssey: A 28-Year Hike on America's Trail

*Blazing Ahead: Benton MacKaye, Myron Avery,
and the Rivalry that Built the Appalachian Trail*

Blast: My Return to Mount Saint Helens

*A Hike in the Woods: Your comprehensive guide to
day hiking gear, clothing, safety and other essentials*

*You Sold Your Book Where? Non-traditional marketing
strategies for breakthrough awareness and book sales*

Hermit
Copyright © 2019 Jeffrey H. Ryan

ISBN: 978-1-63381-188-1

Library of Congress Control Number: 2019910387

All rights reserved. No part of this book may be reproduced in any form or by any electronic or mechanical means, including information storage and retrieval systems, without permission in writing from the author, except by a reviewer, who may quote brief passages in review.

Cover photo of Borestone Mountain at sunrise © 2018 and used with permission of Isaac Crabtree, North Woods Aerial.

Cover design by Puelle Design

Designed and produced by:
Maine Authors Publishing
12 High Street, Thomaston, Maine
www.maineauthorspublishing.com

Printed in the United States of America

To Pam and Scott

Acknowledgments

I started down the path of writing this book by happenstance. Or was it?

When I was working on my first book (an account of hiking the Appalachian Trail over a period of twenty-eight years), an acquaintance gave me an old guidebook to the section of trail that traveled through Maine. The guide had been originally written in the 1930s by Myron Avery, the man most responsible for building the legendary footpath. The guidebook had gone through a number of minor revisions to reflect changes to the route and other details that needed to be brought up to date. While thumbing through the section of the guide entitled "The History of the Trail in Maine," I found reference to a blue-blazed side trail leading to a cabin once owned by a mysterious and colorful character known as Jim Whyte. The description also referred readers who wanted to know more to a 1934 article in the *Boston Sunday Herald*. I quickly set out to find the article. When I received a scanned copy from the Library of Congress, I was amazed by what I read. I knew even then that I'd someday write a book about this extraordinary man.

Finally, in 2018, it was time. I had reached out to Glenn Poole of the Monson Historical Society soon after I found the Jim Whyte article, but I hadn't followed up due to being sidetracked by other projects. Fortunately, he was still available to help and how! Glenn generously shared his local knowledge, his time and a variety of materials that proved indispensable. Tootie and Wayne Bennett (also of the Monson Historical Society) graciously chased down details about Tessa Whyte, even taking special trips to Milo, Maine, to research town files.

The major events in Jim Whyte's life are well documented—sometimes by many sources. But many questions remain. Truth is, the more I learned about Jim Whyte, the more mysterious he became. As with the stories of many legends, much of what I was able to learn about him was rooted in facts, but the trails often became less distinct as I followed them into the past. Regardless, it's been my great pleasure to follow his bread crumbs from New York City to all corners of the earth, then ultimately to Onawa, Maine, in my own backyard.

I wish to acknowledge Roland J. Sawyer Jr. for writing his article "The Mystery of Jim Whyte and his Woodland 'Lookout'" (a piece only made more remarkable by the fact it appears that it was one of the few articles he ever wrote) as well as the other journalists who found the Jim Whyte story compelling and interviewed his contemporaries before they were gone.

No book can take shape without the support and encouragement of friends, family, and colleagues. I am deeply indebted to David Puelle and Kelly Brophy of Puelle Design, who have lent their design talents and insights to all of my projects including the beautiful cover and design elements inside this book; Tom Ackerman, who read early drafts with great enthusiasm and helped get the word out like only he can; and Sarah Fletcher for being a steadfast colleague through the years and making her always incredible and spot-on suggestions for strengthening scenes and characters. The incomparable "is there anything this woman can't do?" Janie Downey Maxwell also deserves great thanks for helping me chase down historical information, providing "fellow author" perspectives, and listening to me prattle on about my book over steaming cups of joe. Special thanks to my sister, Pam Ryan, for her encouragement and love, particularly when some scenes crossed into the realm of biographical.

I often refer to books as being like a lump of clay on a potter's wheel. Once we've gathered the material to create something beautiful, we need to keep working it, throwing out the excess and shaping what's left. If we "overwork the clay," the whole piece falls apart. To that end, my heartfelt gratitude to Stuart Horwitz of Book Architecture for reviewing my first draft and revealing both the strengths and sinkholes in my narrative; to Jane Friedman, one of the smartest people in the publishing world, for helping me keep a healthy perspective about a number of professional conundrums; and to everyone at Maine Authors Publishing for helping me bring this book to fruition.

Jeffrey H. Ryan
May 2019

Table of Contents

Based on a true story.

Bird's Eye View

"I didn't set out to spy on him," Campbell said. "On most nights, the light in his cabin went out an hour or so after dark. Wasn't unusual. Everyone got up with the sun and worked hard all day just to stay alive. From the looks of it, he was no different."

He paused, took a sip of scotch, and continued looking toward the distant ridge, where the tops of the spruce trees were now barely distinct against the late evening sky.

"Yup, if it weren't for that signal, I would never have learned what he was up to."

He leaned back in his seat and put his feet up on the porch railing. Worn wood under his soles marked the hours he spent here—evenings filled with light breezes through the pine boughs above and views across the valley toward Jim Whyte's cabin.

"Strange weather that night. Hotter than hell. It didn't start that way. It was cool when I went to bed. I'd even shut the windows. But I woke up sweating. A hurricane down south was pumping hot air this way. I got up to open all the windows again, then I walked out here onto the porch to see if it was any cooler. That's when I saw the whole thing."

Campbell was still facing straight ahead in his chair. There was no table between us. The wide arms of the Adirondack chairs held our drinks instead, so we were only sitting a few feet apart. I glanced over at him because he'd stopped talking. His head was tossed back, and his eyes were closed, the better to remember that night, I imagined.

"First, I heard the 1:00 a.m. Canadian Pacific train. Nothing strange about that. Happened every other night. Still does. But as it moved through the low spot near Bodfish farm, I saw a light flash from Big Wilson Cliffs. Right over there."

He waved his nearly empty scotch glass out toward the ridge two miles away, and I wondered how his ice cubes stayed onboard. I gazed out that way, too. Nobody lived on Big Wilson Cliffs, but I knew where they were. Even in twilight I could see where the trees on the ridge ended and the bald granite cliffs began.

"I knew the signal was deliberate—three perfectly timed flashes. He was trying to make contact with someone on the train. But I was only able to see one side of the conversation, if you get my drift. I couldn't see the train—the woods were in the way. And even if I could have seen it, I would have been looking at the wrong side. If someone was trying to signal back, I sure wouldn't have seen them from here."

I stood up and walked to the railing to see exactly what Campbell had seen more than a dozen years ago. Of course, he was right. There was nothing visible between his cabin and Big Wilson Cliffs except trees. Even by day, you wouldn't be able to see the railroad tracks, and the roar of Big Wilson Stream was only ever carried here on the wind if it was blowing from the northeast.

"That night, I sat out here looking over toward Big Wilson Cliffs," said Campbell. "But once the train was gone, there was nothing else to see. I don't think Whyte even used the lantern to go back to his cabin. There was nothing but darkness. Of course, I knew he was up to something with somebody on that train. I decided to keep that to myself until I found out more."

Onawa Beckons

I don't remember the first time I went to Onawa. Family legend has it that I was only a few months old when Mom and Dad took me to meet Uncle Roy, so I guess it was the summer of 1919. Of course, Roy got there before the rest of us. He built his cabin on the lake the town is named after just before the turn of the century.

He and Dad were so different, it was hard to believe they were brothers. I guess that happens sometimes. It may have happened otherwise, but I always believed that after their father took his own life, it really pushed them in different directions.

Roy was two years older. He was fourteen and Chet was twelve when they came home from school to find their dad in the barn. From all appearances, he'd shot himself in the head. But the bullet was only the means of death. It was shame that made him pick up the gun. He'd been running himself ragged trying to make that farm pull in enough money to keep a roof over the family. Everything was shaping up for a harvest that would stave off the creditors. Then the heat wave came. Nine straight days of one-hundred-degree heat scorched every row of the corn he was raising for market and half an acre of vegetables that would have kept the family fed over the winter. When he looked out on those fields after the fact, all he could see was a testament to failure.

After his death, the boys' mother Ruth sold the farm and moved to Portland. She bought a house off of Stevens Avenue, close enough so the boys could walk to school. Chet really took to literature and history. Roy was different. He went to classes, all right—his mother made him—but he couldn't wait for the school day to end so he could get busy making something with his hands. By the time he was between junior and senior year, he was already spending summers helping Larry Chandler as part of his carpentry crew.

When the boys graduated from high school, Chet got a scholarship to Bowdoin College just up the road in Brunswick, where he studied his two favorite subjects, and Roy headed north on the train to find a place to build a cabin. When he found Onawa, he knew it was where he wanted to stake his claim.

Roy arrived in Onawa by train—practically everyone did. There were more than forty runs a day through town back then, more than twenty in each direction. It's no wonder Roy ended up working for the railroad, but that came later. He set about building a place to live in first.

The first memory I have of being there took place about thirty yards in front of the porch. I was three years old. Mom was sitting nearby in a chair reading a book, and I was on the grass beneath a birch tree between the cabin and the shore. I remember lying on my back and looking up through light-green leaves swaying against an impossibly blue sky. It's something I never forgot.

As I grew older, I loved going to Onawa. Every time, it seemed Uncle Roy had new, wondrous places to show me—waterfalls, mountain views, and, above all, trout fishing spots. He was full of stories and enthusiasm back then. Lord knows I needed someone to be that way.

Mom used to try to get Dad and me to spend time together—at least enough to help encourage a decent father-and-son relationship. When Dad was doing something like building shelves in the garage, she'd say, "Why don't you go out and ask your father if he needs help?"

I'd go out and ask, always searching for the right moment to interrupt his intense focus on measuring, sawing, or whatever his work required at the time, but he'd always give me the same reply: "No thanks, Ben. I think I can take it from here."

Every time he sent me away, I'd wheel around and walk back inside so he couldn't tell I was disappointed. But Mom always could. "He said he didn't need help," I'd say when I went back into the kitchen. She must have said something to him after each episode, but nothing changed nonetheless. It seemed to me that we were three actors in a two-person play.

After the scene played out dozens of times, I came to realize that Dad's pain was even greater than mine. I learned that I could make my pain go away by reading books, writing stories, or playing catch with my friends. I supposed that was what Dad was doing by building shelves, restoring our house, or completing any of the dozens of projects he always did by himself. But unlike me, he couldn't shut off the pain and move on—the best he could do was hold it at arm's length for a while.

It saddened me that Dad's pain was so deep that he couldn't risk giving his love to more than Mom. But as much as that hurt me, I couldn't blame him for it. His father had abandoned him in the worst way possible, even subjecting him to finding his body in the barn. If that wasn't enough, nearly every friend Dad made in the army had died next to him in an ungodly hail of machine-gun fire, grenade explosions, and mayhem that no man should survive. Some might say that walking off that battlefield in eastern France was a miracle. Perhaps it was. But Dad would never see it that way. He couldn't, or wouldn't, talk about it, even the few times I tried to ask. When I got older, I wished like hell he could have. But he shut that off, too. Just another thing he thought he could handle himself.

The funny thing was he had reason to believe that he could. Dad was the most talented person I'd ever known. He could recite Shakespeare, restore a hundred-year-old house, sail a boat—almost anything he put his mind to—as long as it didn't involve feelings. And there was nothing more uncomfortable than suppertime.

Dinners at home weren't anything like the ones at my friends', where bowls of spaghetti were accompanied by heaps of conversation. Mom was a sensational cook, more of a chef, really. Her Swedish mother had taught her that cooking was a great adventure, an opportunity to get a taste for different cultures without leaving the kitchen, and a way to express love. Thus, we were more apt to eat Swedish meatballs than meatloaf or breakfast frittatas than bacon and eggs. Mom would arrange the food on our (always warmed) plates, place the dishes on the table, and call out "Dinner is ready," the signal for Dad to forsake his latest home project and for me to put my homework aside.

From there, it was always the same routine. We'd marvel at Mom's latest creation—lightly breaded haddock, French onion soup, or whatever she had been inspired to create—then Dad would flip on the radio. Once the tubes warmed up and the sound came through the speaker, there was one abiding rule: "No talking allowed." If you said anything other than "Please pass the butter," you'd be banished from the table. Nothing could prevent Dad from listening to his NBC newscast.

So, every evening during mealtime, I stared at my plate and listened as reporters from far away painted pictures in my imagination. The stories would take me as far from a little dining table in Maine as I could get. I'd wonder what it would be like to be a hog farmer in Iowa or an assembly-line worker at the Ford plant in Detroit. And I fell in love with words. I'd hear new ones like *stock market* or *shanty* and try to remember to ask Mom or Dad what they meant after the news was shut off.

More than anything, I looked forward to the ads. They were clever and fun. I memorized them all. I learned how Doan's Pills "reduced pain due to overexertion or everyday stress and strain" and how Puffed Rice cereal was "shot from guns." It sounds funny, but the ad writers became the dinner companions my parents couldn't be. Later, I'd realize that those kindred souls were nudging me toward a career in writing.

I wondered if Mom ever thought it was strange to eat dinners the way we did. Wouldn't she rather be at a table where people talked about the day or, God forbid, their feelings, like "normal" families did? I never asked. I always assumed she just went along with whatever Dad wanted. Besides, "never asking" was our family's default setting. Mom and Dad insisted that asking people what they thought was like asking them how much money they made—you didn't do it because it was rude and none of your business.

Instead, when we talked, it was almost always brief and almost always about something we'd seen—the safest subject matter imaginable. Tidbits such as "Did you see that Thelma Briggs bought a new car?" or "They're talking about cutting the tree down in front of the town hall" were often enough to bridge the gap between the end of the news and the last bites of dessert. I learned pretty quickly that the best way to contribute was to keep an eye out for things happening around me, then pipe up after the cake or pie was served. My parents would be pleased when I'd report things like seeing the first trillium bloom in the woods behind our house or hearing that Mr. Burke's dog had escaped again, this time boarding the ferry and showing up on Peaks Island. It meant that I knew how family conversation worked in our house and I honored the parameters.

Thank goodness Mom understood that going to Onawa would give me my best chance to gain a wider view.

Uncle Roy

Uncle Roy Harmon enjoyed living on Lake Onawa more than anything else in life. Sometimes I felt like he was on a mission to make sure I loved it as much as he did. If he was, he succeeded.

The cabin he built himself was his base camp. He said that every adventure started when we walked out the front door, which I thought was funny, because to me the adventures started when we got into his canoe. He'd pack a few sandwiches, the fly-fishing gear, a couple of canteens of water, and two life jackets for the trip. He always made me wear my life jacket. It was the only thing I hated about fishing. It was bulky, hot, and smelled like mildewed canvas. But Uncle Roy didn't suffer me complaining. If I didn't stick to the rules, we wouldn't leave the dock.

When we paddled out to fish, Uncle Roy would often tell stories, especially the ones about how the lake was made from a big block of ice that melted and how the face of Borestone was so steep that even a mountain goat would have trouble climbing it. More than anything, though, he talked about fishing.

When I was five years old, he gave me a worm and bobber set for my birthday. When I unwrapped it, I remember Mom asking Uncle Roy if he had really bought it for me or if it was so he'd have a guaranteed fishing buddy. He said it was all for me. And I believed him. He'd help me dig up worms in front of his cabin and bait the hook so I could try to catch sunfish off his dock (always wearing that smelly life preserver, of course). By the time I was eight, he decided I should become a fly fisherman.

Uncle Roy warned me that it would take me a while to learn. He said most people tried to heave a fly through the air like you would a hook and bobber. But it wasn't like that. "You have to make the line do the work," he'd say. He spent hours with me in the clearing out front just casting on the grass with a piece of string tied on the end of the line instead of a real fly. That way, he said, nobody would lose an eye or get part of their earlobe torn off.

He was always patient. That's what made him such a good fisherman and a good teacher. Sometimes I wondered if I'd ever get the hang of casting a fly. It seemed that I was better at leaving big piles of fly line at my feet.

"You know, Ben," he'd say, "learning anything worthwhile is like climbing up a mountain to get a view. Sometimes you have a hell of a time getting up there, but when you make it to the top, when you see the world stretched out in all directions, you forget that your legs and lungs were ever complaining at all."

One early morning, he decided I was ready to try my luck from the end of the dock. A light mist was lifting off the lake, and the trout were rising. You could see circles in the water where they were taking insects off the surface. "Just taking sips," as my uncle was fond of saying. We'd been sitting on the porch looking out at the scene from Uncle Roy's Adirondack chairs. After a minute, he got up and walked over to his fly vest hanging on the wall. He reached into a pocket, pulled out his metal fly box, and selected a fly.

"Ben, I think this should work for you. Here, tie it onto your line."

I wanted him to do it, but he told me if I didn't do it myself it was cheating.

"Now, creep up unto the dock, being as quiet as you can, then cast that fly right to the center of the nearest circle," he said. "I'll sit back here with my coffee and watch."

I tiptoed out to the end of the dock, stripped out some line to work with, just like he'd shown me, then cast toward the circle. The fly sailed through the air, then landed. It was a nice cast, but the fly only made it halfway to the target. I picked the line up off the water, let out some more as it arced behind me, and then cast the rod forward again. This time, the fly landed just beyond the edge of the circle.

Wham! The fly disappeared. I was so surprised I forgot what to do next.

"Set the hook!" Uncle Roy yelled from the porch.

I gave a little tug on the line to make sure my first fish on a fly rod wouldn't get away, then started reeling it in. I was so excited, I was shaking. Uncle Roy was excited, too. He came bounding off the porch with his vest in one hand and a net in the other.

"You got one, Ben! Good job!"

Soon we were both leaning down from the dock to see just what I'd landed. Uncle Roy gently urged the brook trout up to the surface with his net, while never taking it out of the water.

"Nice fish, Ben!" he said.

It was a nice fish, the nicest I'd ever catch, actually. Because it was the first one I ever caught on a fly rod. But it was too small to keep for dinner, and Uncle Roy came to the rescue.

"What do you say we put her back, so she can grow old with us?"

I nodded yes, and Uncle Roy showed me how to take the hook out and then do what he called "reintroducing her to the lake." In a moment, the fish was gone. But the memory of that day was another story. It grew old with me.

I only wish Uncle Roy could have, too.

Campbell Comes Fishing

When my parents and I went up to visit Uncle Roy, it was most often for three days. We'd leave on a Thursday afternoon and come back down to Portland on Sunday night, so Dad would be able to get a good night's sleep before having to go back to work on Monday morning.

Most times, it would be just the three of us and Uncle Roy at the cabin. Every once in a while, Roy's fishing buddy Phil Campbell would stop by to visit. "Campbell," as he was known to almost everyone in the area, was Uncle Roy's age. He'd grown up in a cabin his father had built on a ridge just northwest of Monson—about fifteen miles as the crow flies and another six miles by car. The two of them met where so many people did in the area, Randall's Store. It was pretty inevitable that everyone who lived near Monson would bump into one another either at the store or at church.

Campbell was an even better flycaster than Uncle Roy. The two of them fished together a lot, most often on Lake Onawa because Roy would never have to leave. I asked Campbell about it once. He said that years ago, Uncle Roy would go anywhere to fish with him—Big Wilson Stream, Lake Hebron—wherever the fish were biting. But Roy suddenly decided that Lake Onawa was the only place he wanted to try his luck.

One August afternoon when I was eleven, we were driving back to Portland. I was sharing the back seat with a picnic basket and a pile of wet bathing suits rolled up in towels. Maybe it was because I wished I could have stayed at Uncle Roy's, but I somehow got thinking about how he never left the cabin and we always did.

"How come Uncle Roy never goes anywhere except out on the lake?" I asked.

As soon as I said it, I felt like I'd done something wrong. Mom looked at Dad, and he took his eyes off the road to look at her. It wasn't as if I'd interrupted the nightly news report, but it was pretty bad. Finally, Dad looked into the rearview mirror and said, "Roy leaves the cabin every Monday morning to work on the railroad. I'm sure that after working there every day for a week, he wants to spend as much time as he can at his cabin."

That seemed right, I guess. At least right enough for me not to mention it again until I got older.

The following summer, my folks dropped me off in Onawa to stay with Uncle Roy for two weeks. In time, I would come to realize how important those days were. I had never been so happy. Roy had lived in Onawa for so long that his pace and his philosophy had melded into the place. In the rare times Uncle Roy wasn't fishing with me, I was free to try my luck by myself. The only "rules" were that I had to stay within sight and needed to have my life preserver and an extra paddle onboard. I would hold the life preserver and extra paddle up, he'd nod approval from the porch, and I'd be on my way. I usually stayed close to the shore because the fishing was best there until midsummer when the trout went out to the middle of the lake and stayed deep in the cooler water.

Dinner wasn't always served at six o'clock like it was at home, either. We just ate whenever we were hungry. And even though Uncle Roy didn't have much, he always had food on hand. His garden always had something coming into season—he was vigilant about keeping the deer away and had enclosed his plot with a double-chicken-wire fence and roof. He always said, "It's a matter of survival."

Uncle Roy also presided over an old-fashioned icehouse—a deep, dark hole cut into the side of the hill behind his cabin with a creaky wooden door on the front. Every February, he'd cut blocks of ice out of the lake with a large-toothed handsaw designed for the job. He'd load the ice blocks on a sled, haul them to the icehouse, and stack the place full, always with heaps of sawdust between the blocks to slow down the melting. One of Uncle Roy's hobbies was seeing how late in the year he could still get ice cubes for his drinks from his icehouse. One year, he even made it to September.

Campbell came to visit every evening during the two weeks I was at Uncle Roy's. He kept his fishing gear in his truck and drove over straight from the slate quarry. Uncle Roy had an old fifty-five-gallon drum he'd painted black, hoisted onto the back roof, and filled with water. He'd stuck a spigot into the barrel to create an outdoor shower. When Campbell jumped out of his truck, the slate dust came with him. He was covered in it, and it rose from his clothes as he walked.

"Like beating an old rug with a bat," Uncle Roy said.

Once Campbell rinsed off and put on a change of clothes, he was ready to jump into the canoe with us. I was too young (and light) to sit in the bow or stern, so I sat on a rucksack in the middle.

Sometimes we'd paddle down toward the Onawa train trestle at the far end of the lake, drifting and casting toward the shore at a few well-known spots along the way. When it was just Uncle Roy and me, sometimes we'd go long stretches without saying anything. That certainly changed when Campbell was along. He loved to tell stories! Uncle Roy said it was because he lived alone and had "pent-up demand."

"But you don't have that, Uncle Roy," I said.

"Because some men would rather think than talk," he replied. I wondered how Campbell would feel about that.

Phil Campbell was stocky and tough. Although he was well under six feet tall and weighed what I'd guess to be 225 pounds, he wasn't fat by any means. But he had the biggest head I'd ever seen. An enormous blonde beard that rarely got a trim only added to his imposing presence. He was mighty strong from working in the quarry, too. When he shook my hand, it sure hurt. But, gosh, could that big guy handle a fly rod! I wished I could have watched him more, but he was always sitting behind me—the heaviest guy always sat in the stern. What I did know was that he could place a fly where a fish was rising every time. Uncle Roy was almost as good, but not quite.

We sure had fun those two weeks! When we weren't fishing, we were grilling burgers in the firepit in front of the cabin or talking about what spot on the lake we should fish next. There was only one day we didn't start with fishing. Uncle Roy said we had to spend one full day in the garden pulling weeds and replacing the chicken wire to keep the deer from eating everything. It was the one big job he wanted to do on his two weeks off from the railroad. He told me it was nice to have someone on hand to help spool out the wire and hold it taut against the frame while he hammered the staples home. I felt really good about that.

I never met anyone who had Uncle Roy's energy. It was something you didn't notice right away. He didn't have Campbell's size—like all of us Harmons he was on the small side. But he was built for perseverance. Sometimes after we'd eaten dinner, he'd ask me to wash the dishes so he could go out and pull a few weeds, saw down an overhead branch or something else that helped him go to bed knowing he'd finished another project. No wonder there wasn't an ounce of fat on him.

On the Thursday before my parents arrived to get me, we talked Campbell into fishing Sunset Pond near the top of Borestone Mountain. The pond sat in a saddle surrounded by the mountain's two peaks, and it was one of the most beautiful places to fish in the whole state of Maine.

We paddled the canoe across the lake, hiked up the trail to the pond, and fished until dusk. Every once in a while, I'd look up at the spruce-covered ridges encircling the pond and the slabs of granite that formed the mountain's summit. Chickadees were flitting between branches and chattering their "cheeseburger" calls back and forth. I looked down the shore to my right. Sure enough, the only signs of human beings were the three of us. God, it was beautiful.

The fish were really starting to rise when it was time to leave. Uncle Roy needed to tell me to stop a few times before I reluctantly took my two-piece rod apart and packed my gear for the hike out. As it was, we barely had enough light for us to safely scramble back down to the canoe for our paddle back to Uncle Roy's.

Later on, I'd come to understand that our afternoon and evening on Borestone was more than the highlight of my visit to Onawa that summer. It was the start of an adventure that would last more than twenty-five years.

Uncle Roy's Gift

In 1936, my Uncle Roy sent me a copy of the *Guide to the Appalachian Trail in Maine* for my seventeenth birthday. It was written by a guy named Avery who had grown up in a Maine sardine-factory town called Lubec. Myron Avery was trying to build a walking trail from Georgia to Mount Katahdin, about eighty miles north of Onawa as the crow flies and over one hundred on foot. Most people in the Monson area had heard about Avery. He had led a pack of trail builders through town a few years before. It wasn't hard to pick out Myron Avery. He rolled a bike wheel in front of him as he hiked through the woods. The wheel had a gauge on it that kept track of mileage, and Avery was always taking notes as he went along. Some people said he was odd. Others said he should be admired for making the crazy idea of creating a two-thousand-mile trail come true. Maybe they were both right.

Every time I looked at that guidebook sitting on my bedroom shelf along with half a dozen other titles I vowed to read someday, I wondered why Uncle Roy had bought it for me. He never got a chance to say. They found him dead in front of his cabin just a few days after the package arrived in our mailbox. His heart had given out when he was sawing through a cord of hardwood. I only saw Uncle Roy once the summer before he died. I wished I had seen him more often. I suspected that he sent the book because he wanted me to stay connected to Onawa and the times we had spent fly-fishing on the lake and hiking to the top of Borestone.

At first, his gift became more of an heirloom than an inspiration. I moved it around with me for years without so much as cracking it open. School and work kept me close to Portland, where I had gotten a job in the classified advertising section of the *Portland Evening Express*. The classifieds and the obituary sections were where many of their current writers had gotten their starts. I had always had a reporter's inquisitiveness and a knack for writing stories, so I headed to the newspaper's hiring office two days after I graduated from the University of Maine. I was told that the work would be fast-paced and would give me the chance to someday take my place in the newsroom.

That plan could have gone all to hell with the war, but somehow my number never got called. Given what the last war had done to Dad, I felt relieved, although it wasn't a popular feeling to have at the time. In fact, true to my upbringing, I never said anything about it. Many childhood and college friends had gone into battle. Some had died. Those feelings of loss really hit me hard. As I sat at their funerals, I always wondered why they'd been called up and not me.

Working for the newspaper meant that war stories were always right in front of me. The only interruption in the daily drumbeat of stories was my lunchtime walk to the Forest Avenue post office to pick up my mail and see if it was my turn to report, but somehow D-Day arrived first. When it did, I wondered if the end of "the war to end all wars" really meant that my father would be the last Harmon to ever wear a uniform.

By October of 1946, I had five years in at the newspaper, and I decided to use my remaining week of vacation to take a late-season fishing trip to Onawa. After Uncle Roy died, my folks had inherited his camp. They gave me the key to the padlock, and I ran back to my apartment to pack my gear for the then five-hour ride to the north country on beaten-up back roads. When I got there, I'd have almost nine full days off.

I didn't know what to expect from Onawa. It had been ten years since my parents and I had driven up there to bury Uncle Roy and clean up his cabin. We had gotten rid of his clothing. Most of it had been so worn that we just threw it away. I remembered Mom holding those flannel shirts at arm's length while saying, "Poor Roy, not even enough fabric left in these shirts to clean a window pane with."

Uncle Roy's fishing and camping gear stayed at the cabin. No sense bringing it down to Portland. My folks would go to Uncle Roy's from time to time, and his old friend Campbell would keep an eye on the place in between.

Campbell was one of the few connections I still had with Uncle Roy and Onawa. The others would be Tom and Lydia Randall, who it seemed had scarcely missed a day of running their general store in more than forty years. I was looking forward to seeing the Randalls. Dad would always stop at their store to fill up with gas before we left town for our drive back to Portland. When we went inside, Mom and Dad would end up talking with the Randalls for quite a while, which gave me a chance to look over the penny candy and soda selections. Lydia Randall would see to it that I'd get an extra piece of candy out of the deal. "You need to keep up your strength for the ride home," she'd always say.

It would be good to see Campbell to say hello, and I would certainly stop by Randall's Store to get caught up on local news. But other than that, I planned on long days of fishing and solitude at Uncle Roy's.

As I threw clothing on my bed before stuffing it in duffel bags and a well-used rucksack, I suddenly remembered the guidebook Uncle Roy had given me. At the time, I had no idea that tossing it onto my pile of clothing and fishing gear would be so fortuitous.

Vacation Takes a New Path

I got a late start to Onawa, much later than I had hoped. The packing had taken me longer than expected because I couldn't find my favorite fishing hat. I finally found it stuffed under the front seat of my car. Lord knows how it got there. The good news was that I would likely make it to the cabin before dark, as long as I didn't have to stop for anything but gas. It would be dark by 7:30 p.m., so I couldn't stop to look at the peak foliage along the way other than through my windshield. There'd be time enough to slow down to appreciate the colors over the coming week.

I rolled through town past Tom Randall's store and turned down the twenty-two-mile dirt road to Uncle Roy's camp just before the sun disappeared over the ridge. I was tired from the drive and needed to rally to avoid the puddles and washouts from recent rains. I also had to watch out for moose—this was the time of day they moved from the lakeshore into the woods to bed down for the night.

When I got to Uncle Roy's clearing, I pulled up within eight feet of the back stoop. Using my headlights, I was able to see enough to get the key in the padlock and open the door. The cabin was musty. It had been more than a month since my parents had stayed there, and I opened three windows a few inches to let some air flow through before I made trips to my car to bring in my gear and food for the week.

Once I got everything into the cabin, I didn't feel like unpacking or making any dinner that needed cooking. Instead, I threw together a ham and cheese sandwich, took a bottle of beer from my six-pack, and went out onto the porch.

I sat in one of Uncle Roy's old Adirondack chairs and slid all the way back so I could set my beer and the "church key" I needed to open it on one of the chair's wide arms and my sandwich plate on the other. The last of the daylight was barely lighting the surface of Lake Onawa. The cliffs of Borestone Mountain rose steeply from the opposite shore.

"Not even a mountain goat could climb that cliff," I said aloud.

I thought about the time I had hiked up Borestone with Mom and Dad on one of our three-day visits. Mom and Dad were never that fond of hiking, but I had convinced them it would be fun to see the view from up there. Uncle Roy had to work that Friday, but before he left for the day, he urged my folks to take me up the trail. It took a long time and a lot of rest stops to make it to the top, but both Mom and Dad admitted it was worth it.

I could still remember the spectacular view over the ponds and lakes below, including the railroad trestle at the far end of Lake Onawa. We couldn't fathom how they got the materials and equipment in there to build such a massive bridge, part of the rail line that stretched all the way from Vancouver, British Columbia, to St. John, New Brunswick. It seemed like one of the wonders of the modern-day world tucked into one of the most unlikely places possible.

After my long car ride, it felt nice to be slowing down to the rhythm of Onawa. I was already glad I had decided to come up here away from the noise, the press deadlines, and the ever-present need to make ads fit on three lines or less.

When it was too dark to see anything but Borestone's jagged silhouette and I could only hear the chop, chop, chopping of the waves against the stony shore, I went back inside.

I wasn't quite ready to go to sleep yet, so I lit the kerosene lamp, took my *Guide to the Appalachian Trail in Maine* out of my rucksack, and sat in the most comfortable chair left in the place. I opened the book and thumbed ahead to the section called "Bodfish Farm to Monson." Monson was the only place resembling a town within fifty miles of where I sat. More important to me, it was where Randall's Store was. I figured I could visit Tom and Lydia for a bit, buy some trail snacks, and then hike part of Avery's new trail for the day before coming back to Uncle Roy's.

As I read through the trail description, which included a much-heralded stretch over the Barren-Chairback range northeast of town, one sentence caught my eye. It simply said, "At 3.7 miles, pass blue-blazed side trail leading approximately 3/10 mile to Jim Whyte's Lookout; fine view."

"Jim Whyte," I said aloud. "So that's where he lived."

I had heard the name Jim Whyte before. Campbell had brought him up when he, Uncle Roy, and I were hiking up Borestone with our fly rods to fish in Sunset Pond. In retrospect, I should probably have seen that Uncle Roy's need to stop and rest a few times on the way up had less to do with his age and more to do with his laboring heart.

As we stood high on the mountain's shoulder looking out through the trees, Campbell said, "Reminds me of the view from Jim Whyte's cabin."

"Jim Whyte," said Uncle Roy. "That crazy hermit. It's no wonder he lost his mind."

"He didn't lose his mind," said Campbell. "He lost his voice. Then he went down south to die."

"Who's Jim Whyte?" I asked.

"Never mind. Just a crazy hermit who lived in a cabin a dozen miles from here. You don't need to know more than that," said Uncle Roy. He nodded toward the trail to simultaneously urge the fishing trip forward and put a halt to any discussion about Jim Whyte.

Fifteen years later, sitting in Uncle Roy's chair, I chuckled at the irony. The book he sent me as a gift was reintroducing me to Jim Whyte—a name I otherwise may have never thought of again.

I set the guidebook down, stood up, and stepped onto the porch. It was a crisp night. There were no clouds to keep the day's warmth from escaping to the heavens. The stars were as bright as I'd ever seen them. I walked out into the clearing and tilted my head back to look straight above me. Then I had an idea. I went over to the old birch tree by the shore, lay down on my back, and looked up through the leaves at the stars above. The slight breeze moving the leaves in front of the stars created a mesmerizing display similar to blinking lights. I lay with my hands behind my head and thought about nothing except the satisfaction of being right where I was.

After a while I started chilling down, so I stood up, zipped my jacket all the way to my chin, and leaned against the birch, looking across the lake toward the cliffs of Borestone. I couldn't make out any features except the dark form of the mountain rising to meet the stars. I started turning around to go back inside for the night. But something made me look left toward the adjacent ridge that I had only known as part of a wide swath of forest stretching toward Canada. Until today, I hadn't fully realized that somewhere in that forest, a mysterious man had settled down to carve out an existence.

Even the very little I had to go on was enough to intrigue me. Who was this "crazy hermit"? Why did he come to Onawa? How long did he live here? How did he lose his voice? Why did Campbell seem to stick up for his character? And why was Uncle Roy so dismissive of him?

As I walked back toward the porch, I already had a plan. As soon as daylight came, I'd set out to discover Jim Whyte's cabin.

Randall's Store

I woke up just as the sun's first rays were lighting the treetops on Borestone's summit. I stepped out onto the porch and looked out toward what was once Uncle Roy's garden. The chicken wire we'd replaced years ago was gone. So was the wooden frame. Maple and pine branches had overtaken the airspace above. Making sure his garden got enough sun had been an important yearly ritual. But a man's place in the sun is no match for nature's plan. Other than the cabin and a slate marker in the Monson cemetery, the story of Roy Harmon's time on earth would soon be hard to follow. I wondered if Jim Whyte's would be, too.

I'll never know if I stay on this porch, I said to myself. I'd better get going.

Monson used to be a slate town. When Welsh immigrants arrived in 1870 and discovered a vein of deep black slate, they launched an industry that created roof shingles, countertops, and cemetery plot monuments for customers all over the world. But when the Great Depression came along, Monson's slate mining almost came to an end. Some of the workers moved out of town. Many stayed to work in the woods. Harvesting trees to feed the insatiable demand of paper mills was always an option for Mainers seeking work.

To be sure, the Monson economy wasn't what it was when the slate business was booming. The dozen or so buildings that lined Main Street were looking tired. At the very least, a coat of fresh paint would have gone a long way. But I knew that it wasn't lack of pride or motivation that was keeping people from getting around to sprucing up their homes and businesses. The financial and psychological double whammy of the Great Depression had left deep scars. Just like Uncle Roy's garden, it took an incredible amount of energy to keep the town prospering. As it stood, there just wasn't enough of anything—young folks, jobs, money, or energy—to bring it back. Only time would tell whether Monson could rebound or whether everyone had scattered for good, lured away by towns with greater opportunities.

I thought about how fortunate I was to have a steady job and a decent income with one of the state's largest employers. As beautiful and peaceful as it was in this part of the state, I was unsure how I would fare over winters where the snow routinely blanketed the ground from mid-November until May.

I pulled up to the curb at Randall's Store and went inside. In the decade since I had been there, not much had changed. Tom was even stationed in the same place I last saw him, hunched over the counter glancing through the sports section. He looked up and smiled when he saw it was me coming through the door.

"Ben! I wondered when you'd make it up here. Last time I saw your folks, they said it was on your mind to get up to Roy's cabin for some fishing. It's been so long since I've seen you, I wondered if you'd ever make it up here again."

"May be a bit more hiking than fishing this time, Tom. It's pretty windy out on the lake, and I want to check out Myron Avery's new trail, anyway."

Tom cleared the newspaper aside, stood straight up with his fingertips pressing against the counter like he so often did, then shook his head back and forth a few times. "Avery," he said. "That guy sure is driven. It's crazy enough to try building a trail from here to Georgia, let alone when the country barely had a few pennies to rub together. I thought he was crazy. But, you know, I heard he almost has the whole thing done. I wonder if anyone will actually walk on the thing."

"Well, I'll do my part," I said. "At least around here. I also want to check out the side trail to Jim Whyte's lookout."

That comment sure took Tom Randall by surprise. He took his hands off the counter, placed them by his side and took half a step back.

"Jim Whyte?" said Tom. "How do you know about him?"

"Phil Campbell mentioned him once when he, Uncle Roy, and I were hiking up Borestone."

"Huh," said Tom. He paused for a few seconds as he rubbed his chin between his right-hand thumb and forefinger. "I don't know why you'd want to go over there. Don't get me wrong—the view is nice and all, but I heard his cabin is just a pile of old logs. The thieves got in there right after he left town. Tore the place to shreds."

By then I'd moved to Tom's deli counter to survey the snacking options. "Could you wrap up a quarter-pound of sharp cheddar and a piece of smoked sausage for me, Tom? Just enough for a decent lunch on the trail?"

As Tom went to work on my order, he opened up a bit about Jim Whyte. "You know," he said, "if you ask around, you'll hear a lot of things about Whyte. Most people don't know what they're talking about. He was hard to get to know, especially at first, so people made up all sorts of wild stories about him. In the early years, I was one of the few people in town he'd talk to. He didn't have much choice, really. I was the only place to stock up on food, mousetraps, and other stuff."

"So, you know the real story," I said.

"I do. But I can't talk about it. Not now, anyways. In a few minutes, this place will start getting busy. On Saturday mornings practically everyone comes into town to get something. Why don't you check out Whyte's lookout today, then come over to my house for lunch tomorrow? Lydia is heading to Skowhegan to visit a friend after church, and I've spread the word that I'll be closing the store at noon, so I can take a few hours off. If you swing by around twelve-thirty, we'll have time to catch up on what's happened around town since the last time you were here."

"Sounds good to me," I said. "I'll give a full accounting of the cabin, or what's left of it."

Jim Whyte's Lookout

A little northwest of Monson, I turned onto the dirt road that led to the trail. It wasn't hard to find if you looked closely for the place where the path crossed the road. Avery and his crew had marked the Appalachian Trail by painting marks, each two inches wide by six inches high, on trees. If you saw a white "blaze" up ahead, you knew you were still on the path. If you saw two of them, one above the other, you knew that either the trail was about to abruptly change route or that you were about to meet up with a side trail.

I got out of the car and walked around to the passenger door to get my pack off the front seat. It was a gorgeous fall day—breezy, but not so windy that it would drive all the leaves out of the trees. Those harsh, late-autumn winds would come soon. But for the first several days I was in Onawa and Monson, the landscape would showcase its peak mix of intense oranges, yellows, and reds. I shouldered my pack and set off down the Appalachian Trail for the first time.

Avery's crew had done a thorough job marking the trail, which was a good thing because the path wasn't worn enough yet to navigate without using blazes. True to Tom Randall's prediction, not enough people had hiked on it yet to make the path unmistakable.

The first section was muddy. I was glad I wasn't hiking here in June or July. The blackflies and mosquitoes would have been fierce. Soon enough, I began climbing up on slate ledges to escape the bog and reach the intersection with the trail to Jim Whyte's lookout. When I got there, I was out of breath. I stopped and thought of that day when Uncle Roy, Campbell, and I had taken that break on Borestone—the day I first heard the name Jim Whyte. I turned and looked through the trees behind me. Sure enough, I could make out the shape of the mountain sticking up like a shark's fin. I wondered again why Uncle Roy had been so dismissive of Jim Whyte, why he had waved his hand as if the hermit lived a dozen states away, not less than eight miles. Why had a hermit living way back in the woods bothered him at all?

The side trail over to the lookout stayed faithful to the ridge, a scramble across an enormous granite slab topped by spruce trees. The loggers left these stands alone. The trees were too hard to get to and too small to deal with—there wasn't enough soil to sustain them through middle age, and they took a pounding from the wind and snow, which stunted their growth. They toppled over so often that it wasn't worth painting blazes on them. The trail was now marked with blue blazes painted on rocks and with piles of stones called "cairns" instead.

After about a half mile, the trail dropped off of Big Wilson Cliffs, then climbed back up to emerge into a great clearing filled with shin-high grass and small boulders. Toward the back of the clearing, up against the woods, was something completely unexpected—Jim Whyte's cabin, standing in one piece.

"Pile of logs," I muttered. It looked like Tom Randall had gotten that part of the story wrong. But as I approached the building, I realized the description "pile of logs" wasn't too far off the mark.

I walked up onto the porch and set my pack down. The front door had two planks nailed over it forming the letter X. The thieves had pried the hasp from the doorframe. The door was missing, so the planks really didn't serve a purpose other than creating an informal barrier to entry. I didn't want to remove them. My instinct was to honor the owner—whoever it now was.

A lot of people owned cabins in the Maine woods. Some lived there year-round. Others built them as their hunting and fishing camps—places they'd visit for various lengths of time as their livelihoods would allow. There was an unwritten law about camps. You honored the owner's property. Even if the door didn't have a lock on it, you didn't step inside. The only exception was if it would save your life. Everyone in the area knew stories about people who had fallen through the ice, miraculously pulled themselves out of the water, then thawed out at some stranger's cabin. In 1939, a twelve-year-old boy named Donn Fendler got lost when he was climbing Mount Katahdin with his father, his uncle, and his brother. After nine days of wandering around in the remote Maine woods—thirty-five miles from where he wandered off the trail, sixteen pounds lighter, and close to death—he stumbled upon a hunting camp. It saved his life.

I hopped down from the porch and walked around to the side of the cabin. There were two window casings on the first floor. The rear one had all its windowpanes. The front one brought a chuckle. There was nothing there except a hole. The vandals had removed the window, frame and all. A boulder placed beneath it allowed a not-so-graceful entry. Should I accept the open invitation?

I chose to move on.

Behind the camp was a well-worn path to the outhouse. There was no doubt that Jim Whyte was a year-rounder. From the looks of it, he had been one for some time. Unlike the cabin, the outhouse had been left alone. Instead of a padlock, an old stick had been slipped through the hasp to keep the door shut. I took the stick out, shoved it in my pants pocket, and opened the door.

"Yup. Your standard outhouse," I said. The only thing distinctive about it was that someone had written something in German on the inside of the door—an inspirational phrase of some kind. It had been written there with purpose. The letters were spaced evenly, and the script was smooth. I couldn't imagine that someone had written it on the door after it was in place. There was hardly enough room to stand between the door and the throne. It had to have been done when the door was lying flat, most likely when it was built. Had Jim Whyte been the artist?

I closed up the door and put the stick back in place. As I walked the path back toward the cabin, something didn't seem right. I stopped walking, looked around, and immediately realized what it was. The path wasn't much more worn than everything around it. Usually, the forest floor is undisturbed because it's easier to stay on the path. But here behind Jim Whyte's, where there would normally be large mats of moss and a certain continuity to the landscape, there were unmistakable signs of human disturbance. Someone—more likely many someones—had been digging holes in a wide, random pattern about seventy-five feet wide in all directions. It wasn't as if Jim Whyte had been looking for a new spot to move the outhouse. And it made no sense that he would put a garden here—it was too shady, and the soil was uneven and thin. These were the marks left by people looking for something.

I suddenly remembered my pack and decided to go back to the cabin porch to eat my lunch. It wasn't as if anyone was likely to show up and steal my pack. But the idea of people up here digging around had reminded me that I'd be more comfortable keeping it in plain sight.

Up to that point, I hadn't felt much of a connection to Jim Whyte. But the view from his porch changed that. Until then, I hadn't paused to see the world from his perspective. I had been too obsessed with the status of his front door and the possibility of getting in. But after sitting on his porch with my legs dangling over the edge, I understood why he'd never want to leave. The view was indescribably beautiful—mountains rippling out in all directions, valleys filled with fall splendor, and awe-inspiring silence.

I sat for a long time trying to burn Jim Whyte's view into my memory and straining to pick out familiar landmarks. Borestone was so close that it seemed I could reach out and touch it. I had never seen the mountain from this side before. I had only seen the stark, impressive cliffs rising out of Lake Onawa and the view from its summit, where granite and ponds were the outstanding features. But from Jim Whyte's porch, the mountain showed a softer side—it was so completely blanketed in spruce that it was hard to pick out any rock features at all. I turned to look across the valley. The low mountains rippling out to meet the far horizon were impressive, but it was the sky that made me gasp. It was one of those rare views that had the power to make you feel humbled. I imagined Jim Whyte sitting out here every night as the stars lit up the expanse above. It made me want to come back and camp here to see it for myself. I figured nobody would mind if I spread out my bedroll here.

After lunch, I went back to the window with the boulder beneath it. Climbing up to look through the window seemed reasonable enough. I was soon in limbo, squatting on my haunches in an empty window frame—straddling the line between casual observer and trespasser. The place had been thoroughly picked over, but not completely vandalized. The thieves seemed to have a line that even they wouldn't cross. The pots and pans had been stolen, but the cookstove was left alone. The walls were bare, except for the dozens of nails that had once held whatever Whyte needed to have handy. All the windows were intact except the one they had removed. The front door was still in one piece but had been leaned against an inside wall. The damage seemed more the work of souvenir hunters than thieves. If whoever did this was vindictive, they would have taken everything, then perhaps burned the cabin down. Instead, they just took everything they could carry out.

Even with most of the necessities for daily life removed, or maybe because of it, I was struck by the precision of the woodwork through-out the cabin. Whoever built this place knew what they were doing. The joints were tight. The wallboards and floorboards were butted up snuggly to one another. The builder had taken the time to make sure they were so.

I couldn't stay squatting in the window frame any longer. As I low-ered myself back to the boulder, I thought of Uncle Roy's cabin. I wouldn't want anyone to trespass there. I was pleased I didn't jump down into Jim Whyte's, even if it was just to take a deeper look. It wasn't my place.

Secrets Shared, Promises Kept

Tom Randall and his wife Lydia lived in a house they bought on Lake Hebron. It was the second home they owned in Monson. They had lived in an old farmhouse on the Tenny Hill Road for eighteen years when they first got to town and took over what used to be Ormsby's General Store. I had never been in their house before, but I knew where it was. Uncle Roy had told me one day when we were out in his canoe. Like so many places up here, the Randall place had originally been built as a camp, then insulated and expanded to become a year-round home.

Tom was waiting for me at the door. As I approached him, I noticed how gray his hair had become. All my life I'd known him to sport thick, brown hair. When I last saw him ten years ago, I remember thinking how he never changed. Now in the full light of day, I realized for the first time that he was starting to look his age. I didn't want him to feel self-conscious about it, so I stepped back a few paces and pretended to be taking in the front of the house.

"Sorry I'm a few minutes late. I actually drove past your driveway a bit and had to turn around. I thought you were farther down the shore."

"That's understandable," said Tom as we stepped inside. "The road side of our place isn't much to look at and is hidden a bit by trees. We put most of our energy into making the lake side nice." He waved his hand toward the kitchen stove. "You drink coffee? I just brewed a pot."

"Boy, do I," I said. "The more, the better."

Tom laughed. "Well, you couldn't do much better than visiting the top coffee seller in Monson," he said.

After some small talk about goings-on in town and my job with the newspaper, Tom offered that it was time to switch gears.

"Let's move out onto the porch," he said. "We aren't going to get many more warm days like this between now and next spring, and I spend too much time inside, anyway."

As Tom opened the door to step outside, he kept on talking. "I'll tell you, Ben, Lydia and I have really enjoyed owning the store, but owning a store is like farming. You're pretty tied down to the place. We can't leave for more than a few days at a time. Every once in a while, I need to take an afternoon off. Today seemed as good a time as any."

He set the coffeepot on a couple of hot pads he had brought out with him and gestured toward a seat. "Pull up a chair," he said. "Did you get up to Jim Whyte's clearing yesterday?"

"Yes. But his cabin wasn't a pile of logs. It was in pretty good shape," I said.

"Really? That's not what I'd heard."

"From who?"

"Fred Hall and a bunch of his hunting buddies stopped by the store to buy some beer last fall. They were coming back from a day of tramping around in the woods over there. Fred said they had decided to climb up to Jim Whyte's. They probably got there the same way you did, although they didn't say."

Tom took a slug from his coffee cup, then continued on. "Hall said there was nothing left to the cabin except a pile of logs. From what you say, that's not so."

"Far from it," I said. "The place is empty, but it's in good shape. The vandals took out a window to get in. They also broke the front door lock. They likely did that first. But if someone wanted to move in, they'd only need to fix the door and replace the window. Even the cookstove is ready to go."

"Well, I guess Hall's definition of 'a pile of logs' is different from mine," said Tom. He clapped his hands together once, then held them in front of his belly. "Well, we're not here to talk about Fred Hall. You want to know about Jim Whyte."

Tom looked out over the lake for a few seconds, then up into the sky. He seemed to be sifting back through memories until he arrived at the right one. Just like Uncle Roy, he didn't look you in the eye until he decided what he wanted to say.

"Lydia and I bought the store from Charlie Ormsby in 1892. He agreed to help teach us how to run it over the first winter, but Charlie wasn't helping us anymore, so it had to be the spring of '93 when Jim Whyte walked through the door. At first, I didn't know he wasn't from around here. How could we? Even though we'd lived in Monson for a while, we hadn't gone through a spring and summer of owning the store, so we didn't know for sure who was from here, who was from away, and who came up here from time to time.

"After the fact, we both realized this guy probably wasn't from anywhere near Monson or maybe even from Maine. I was stocking shelves in the middle of the store when he walked in, so I had a clear view of him from head to toe. I'd guess he was in his mid-thirties. He was what I guess you'd call average height, but he was also nimble and strong, befitting a guy who worked in the woods or fields. He wore a watchman's sailor cap. One of those navy ones with the rolled-up bottom. And he wasn't wearing a coat, just a flannel shirt. I remember thinking that was unusual because it was only about forty degrees out. It was only when he went back outside and walked away that I saw his pack. It was so loaded with stuff that it looked bigger than he was."

I had a pretty good idea why Jim Whyte hadn't been wearing a coat. If his pack was that heavy and he walked into town with it on his back, a coat would be overkill.

"Was he sweating?" I asked.

"Not that I recall," said Tom.

Either someone dropped him off just outside town or he took the train as far as Onawa, I thought as Tom continued his story.

"Lydia says she remembers his eyes—pale blue and bright as Lake Hebron. She was behind the counter when he first walked in and asked her if we stocked meats and cheeses. She always claims she knew there was something mysterious about that man from the start. It was more than the fact that he didn't want to talk much, she said. More of a feeling that this man was wiser than his years and had more going on than he'd ever be willing to share. But just between you and me, she didn't say anything about her observation until we found out more about him. But I'm getting ahead of things."

Tom picked up the coffeepot and raised his eyebrow. It was his way of asking me if I wanted more without having to stop talking. I waved my hand over the top of my cup. I had already had a full pot of "roadtar blend" before I'd left Uncle Roy's and my right foot was bouncing up and down. Tom topped off his cup, took a big sip, and resumed his tale.

"That day, he said he was going into the woods to scope out some hunting spots, so he could come back later that year after the season started. It wasn't an unusual thing to do, so we didn't give it much thought. He ended up buying what you bought from me yesterday—some cheese and some smoked sausage. He paid his bill, shoved the food in the top of his pack, walked out the door, and turned left to walk up Main Street. That was the last we saw of him. And it was also the last time I didn't try to find out a customer's name. Like I said, neither of us felt like the man was dangerous or anything. There's just a sense of neighborliness that comes out when you know someone by name. He never did come back to hunt that year, at least as far as anyone knows. But two years later, he came back to Monson for good."

"For good?" I asked. "How long was that?"

"Not yet," said Tom. "We'll get to that."

Tom was in his seventies. He reminded me a lot of Uncle Roy. They had been contemporaries. But they were also storytellers who hated to be interrupted. The tale needed to be told the way they needed to tell it. If you interrupted once, you were gently reminded not to. If you interrupted again, it was at the risk of never hearing the rest of the story at all. If there would be a time for asking questions, it would be on Tom's terms.

"It was August of 1895. This time, he brought a woman with him. That intrigued both of us, but especially Lydia. She wanted to make small talk with the woman the stranger simply referred to as 'my wife.' But eventually we'd find out that her name was Dora and his was Jim Whyte. We'd also find out that he didn't come up here in 1893 to scope out hunting spots. He was here to buy a piece of land—and he did. The parcel between Little Wilson Stream and Big Wilson Stream, where he built his cabin. All that fall, people could hear the chopping of his axe and the sound of his crosscut saw from up on the ridge."

"He was quite the carpenter," I said. "I wonder where he learned that."

Tom glanced over, nodded, and kept talking. I realized I could chime in if my words fit in just so.

"They built a trail up to the ridge. They even built a wooden bridge over Big Wilson Stream, which was more for them than anything. They didn't like visitors back then, that's for sure."

When Tom emphasized the words *back then*, he looked at me with that "don't interrupt me, I'll get back to it" look that was designed to keep my inquisitiveness at bay.

"They hardly ever came down off that hill. All that winter and into the spring. Jim and Dora Whyte only came down to buy things at the store. They certainly never went to church. And that got people talking. Who was this couple? Where did they get their money? Even for a town that pretty much leaves people to their own business, the legend of Jim Whyte started to grow. People were always asking Lydia and me what they bought at the store and why they hardly ever came down off the hill. At first, Jim Whyte said that they'd socialize once the cabin got built. That helped stem the tide for a while. But after a time, it wasn't working as an excuse anymore. That's when your uncle and Campbell went up there to take a look around."

"Uncle Roy? He never said anything about that," I said.

"That's another thing to ask Campbell about," said Tom. "He was there. I wasn't. Better to hear his version. I'll probably get it wrong like that 'pile of logs' that used to be Jim Whyte's cabin."

I wondered why Campbell had never mentioned Jim Whyte other than that time on Borestone Mountain. True, Phil Campbell spent a lot of time alone, but it wasn't like he never told stories, especially if he'd had a few drinks. Uncle Roy's silence was even harder to understand. We'd spent dozens of days fishing together and even more around the campfire, and he never mentioned the odd man from out of town. But why? Even I could already tell that Lydia Randall was right from the beginning. Jim Whyte had a secret—probably more than one.

"The confounding thing about Jim Whyte is how little anyone knew about him for so long," said Tom. "Come to think of it, that goes for him and his wife, if she *was* his wife. Nobody knows for sure. What everyone does know is that in the summer of '96, less than a year after arriving here with Jim Whyte, Dora left town. One Monday morning, she came down off the mountain with her luggage and boarded the train out of Onawa. Word was she was heading back to New York. That's the story that stuck, anyway."

"So, Jim became a hermit?" I asked.

Tom let out a laugh that caught me by surprise.

"If you can call a married man a hermit," he said. "I don't think it was more than a month before another woman moved in with him. They say she came from Milo and that her name was Tessa. Nobody knows how they met, but I guess they were a better match 'cause that woman lived with him up there for twenty years. And the only time she ever came down from that cabin was when they left together to visit Whyte's mother in New York City a few times a year. If she ever went anywhere else with him, nobody knew about it. Jim Whyte came down to the store every couple of weeks, at least. I think she was more of a hermit than he was."

The more I heard, the stranger the story became. Why would Tessa Whyte sign up for a life of desolation on a Maine mountaintop, even if it was beautiful desolation?

"The thing was, they had money. Sometime in the early 1900s—I think it was after the snow melted in the spring of 1903—Jim Whyte told me that he and Tessa were going to New York. They came back with a wagon full of so many packages on it I can't believe the axles didn't snap under the load. Everyone figured it was some kind of inheritance, although it wasn't from his mother, because she was still alive. People said those boxes contained books, glassware, linens, and all kinds of things that wealthy folks from New York would have. Maybe being surrounded by all that finery made them never want to leave the cabin. They certainly didn't have to."

Tom excused himself to go to the bathroom. While he was gone, I thought about what I'd learned so far. I just couldn't understand hardly ever coming down off that hill. I knew how beautiful it was. I had been there. Maybe I just didn't understand hermits. I had met a number of colorful characters in Monson who depended on the land to make a living—slate miners, lumbermen, and farmers among them. Every one of them had some kind of connection with the community. They helped one another as neighbors and friends. It's what you did to make it through the Maine seasons. I couldn't imagine living in complete isolation, even if I had a partner and even if I was wealthy.

Tom came back to the deck carrying a plate of cookies. "Almost forgot. Lydia baked these last night and wanted me to be sure to offer you some. Don't make a liar out of me."

I was starving. I hoped they were anything but peanut butter cookies. I really detested those.

"They're peanut butter," said Tom.

I had to eat at least one. I'd been taught that you had to eat anything a host offered you. As Tom launched into the Jim Whyte story again, I turned away and swallowed a big chunk of the cookie whole to sneak it past my taste buds.

"One day, she left. Just like Dora had long before her," he said. "Nobody ever saw Tessa Whyte again. Twenty years in Monson, then the mystery woman was gone. Things started changing after that."

"Changing how?" I asked. I turned away, swallowed the other half of the cookie, and poured more coffee to wash away the taste of peanut butter that I hoped would go the way of Tessa Whyte.

"You'll have to ask Campbell about that. The only thing I know is that Jim's spending habits began to change," he said.

"Campbell? What does he have to do with anything?" I asked.

"That's for him to say. What I can tell you is what I saw. He needs to tell you the rest."

Tom took a bite from a peanut butter cookie and a bunch of crumbs fell onto the floor. He didn't notice and kept on talking.

"After Tessa left, Jim Whyte started coming into the store more often. He also started staying longer and even swapping a few yarns. Before that, he always seemed to be in a hurry to get back to his cabin."

"What year did Tessa leave?"

"Let me see." Tom did that "look to the heavens" thing again, searching for a clue. "It was the same year Andy Sprague's daughter Emma died, poor thing. I remember it was a late spring day. Everyone was making their way to the church for the service. I was preparing to lock up the store when Tessa Whyte walked in alone. You could have knocked me over with a feather. I'd never seen her without Jim Whyte."

Just then, there was a noise from inside the house. Lydia had returned from her shopping trip.

"Lydia, what year did Emma Sprague die?" yelled Tom.

"Well, isn't that a lovely welcome home subject?" she said. "It was the spring of '17. Remember? Her boyfriend, Jimmy Chase, got sent to France to fight later that year. Oh, Ben, did Tom offer you some of my cookies?"

"Yes, he did. And they were so good I wolfed them down," I said.

"Good. I have more."

"All set, thank you."

Lydia went back into the house and I reminded Tom where we had left off. "Tessa Whyte," I said.

"Yes, Tessa Whyte." He sighed as he said her name. "I had never really studied her face. How could I? I scarcely had the chance. But this time, without even exchanging words, I knew that her time in Monson was over. I could see she was having a hard time asking for help. I was about to say something when she asked if there was any way she could get a ride to Milo. As I stood there thinking, I realized how little I had spoken to her over the years."

Tom peered back toward the kitchen to make sure Lydia was out of sight, then said, "And what a beauty she was."

"I heard that, Tom Randall!" said Lydia. "But I suppose I can't blame you for saying it."

Sensing that Tom was about to get into deeper trouble, I tried to keep the story moving along. "How did she leave town?" I asked.

"Jim Melcher had just finished his bread delivery. He was still parked across the street, writing some things down, I imagine, when Tessa Whyte had walked in. I ran out from behind the counter and hailed Jim just before he drove off. I placed two small rolls and a piece of cheese in a bag and handed them to Tessa. Something to take on her journey. She climbed up into the front seat of Melcher's wagon and that was it. She was gone."

"And what about Jim Whyte? When did he leave?"

"Jim Whyte stayed for a while. More than a dozen years more, as it turned out."

"And he got friendlier?"

"Yup. He spent less and he talked more is the way I'd put it. He never talked a lot, but there were some things that he knew about that really surprised me. Sailing, for example. I would never guess that he had spent a fair amount of time on a ship. Why would I, being this far inland?"

Tom got up from his chair. "I need to show you something. Stay right here," he said. He went into the house and returned with something in his hand. "Whyte gave me this," he said. "Go ahead, take a look."

I held the brass telescope in my hands. It was beautiful. The leather wrapping had seen steady use but was nowhere near worn through.

"Go ahead," said Tom. "Take a look through it."

I extended it to full length, peered across the lake, and twisted the eyepiece section to sharpen the focus. The image was amazingly clear.

"They call it a 'three draw' because of the three sections that pull out of it," said Tom. "Whyte got it when he was a young man at sea. One day, he showed up at the store and handed it to me."

I stopped looking through the telescope and started looking at it instead. It held even more intrigue as an artifact of Jim Whyte than as a precision instrument. This man was becoming more mysterious by the day. Here was a hermit once obsessed with privacy who suddenly decided to mingle with townsfolk. But not just any townsfolk, the two most well-known people in the community. It was also curious that of all the gifts Whyte could have given to the storekeeper, he chose to give up the one that he had used to keep an eye on the world around him. The one he had used to help him stay safely to himself.

"By 1923, I'd gotten to know enough of Jim Whyte to trust him with running the store for a few days here and there. Like I said before, when you run the store and post office, you don't get to leave much. But I had come to trust Jim by then. He rarely drank, and if he said he was going to be somewhere, he was always on time."

As Tom was recounting those days at the store, Lydia walked out onto the porch with a cushion in hand, set it in the empty wooden chair next to me, and sat down to join the conversation.

"Tom and I talked a lot about whether we could trust Jim to run the store and post office while we took a few days off," she said. "I didn't want us to let our guard down just because we so needed some time off. But in the end, we decided that what we knew about him seemed to make up for the parts of him he wanted to hide."

"I trusted him enough to swear him in as interim town clerk so he could run the post office," said Tom. "When we found out some of the other jobs he had held in his lifetime, it seemed only appropriate that he was in charge of the mail for a while, too."

"What other jobs?" I asked.

"You'll need to ask Campbell about that."

"Why do you keep bringing up Campbell?" I asked.

As soon as I said it, I thought I sounded a little more annoyed than I should have. But I really wanted to hear the story from Tom. He was easy to talk to. I wasn't sure Campbell would be as easy to get the story out of. "I just figure you probably know more about Jim Whyte than Campbell does, being that you own the store and all," I said. It wasn't how I really felt, but it sounded good.

"Ben, everyone wanted to know what brought Jim Whyte to Onawa and what he was up to after he got here. But now there are only three people left who know the story—Lydia, me, and Phil Campbell. You need to hear it from him, if he's willing to share it."

I looked over at Lydia, but she wasn't about to look at me. She just kept staring out at the lake until Tom started talking again.

"One time I made the mistake of letting something out about Jim Whyte that I shouldn't have. After that, I promised Campbell that it would never happen again. That's all I'll say about it for now. I can't say more until you talk to him."

Tom got up from his chair, and Lydia followed suit. I wasn't expecting things to suddenly turn so awkward, but Lydia came to the rescue.

"Oh, Ben, why don't you take this sack of cookies? Maybe you can take them with you when you go to see Campbell. He loves cookies."

I thanked her and turned toward Tom to gauge his mood.

"I'm sorry I had to cut you off there, Ben, but Lydia and I can't share any more until you talk to Campbell. It's how we left things with him years ago."

"I understand," I said. "I'll get over to see Campbell before I leave town. Thank you both for your hospitality."

Lydia wanted to make sure things were fine. "Promise us you'll stop by the store before you go back to Portland," she said, reaching for my hand.

"I promise," I said. "I promise."

The Randalls stood in the door and waved as I backed out of the driveway. They needn't have worried. I wasn't mad—a tad frustrated, maybe, but not upset. I knew they were good people who were keeping their word with Campbell.

I drove back toward town and turned left on Main Street. There was a dirt road a quarter mile outside of town where I could sit and think about what to do next and jot down some notes about what Tom Randall had shared about Whyte. The thought of taking notes when I was there seemed rude. But there were things, dates mostly, that I wanted to retain as reference points.

From when I was a toddler, I had been blessed with a near photographic memory. The ability to relive scenes in my life in great detail was a gift that would always serve me well as a storyteller. Two years after the fact, if you asked me what color shirt Tom Randall was wearing when we had coffee or what patterns of light and shadow the midday sun created on Tom and Lydia's porch, I could tell you right away. But I couldn't retain numbers worth a damn. Case in point: if you asked me what year Tom and Lydia bought Ormsby's General Store and went to work, or what year Dora left town, I wouldn't be able to remember.

Consequently, all the way to the dirt road, I replayed my conversation with the Randalls. When I found the right spot, I pulled to the side of the road, shut the engine off, took a pencil from above the visor, and looked for a scrap of paper. A piece of brown grocery bag did the trick. I scribbled down the five important dates from our chat.

1893—Jim Whyte buys land

1895—Returns with Dora

1896—Dora leaves town
1896—Tessa shows up
1917—Tessa leaves Monson

Once I wrote the dates down, I felt a sense of relief. Both parts of the story—the narrative and the numbers—were safe now. It was the familiar sense of accomplishment I felt when the last dish was washed and put away or I took the dry flies off my fishing vest and put them back in the fly box so they'd be ready for the next time the fish were rising. I didn't know what would happen with the Jim Whyte story, but I wanted all the pieces to be in place and accessible.

"Now what?" I asked myself aloud. I looked between the mud spatters on my windshield down the dirt road leading to Onawa. There was no sense in washing the car until I got back to Portland. Dust and mud were part of life up here in the wilds. Up here, people let rain do most of the car-washing. The rain was due to roll in toward the end of the week. But today was Monday, and the only clouds were billowing fair-weather ones, riding across the sky and creating temporary shadows on the orange landscape below.

Down in Portland, the time clock made my schedule. I had to punch in every weekday by 8:00 a.m. Up here, the weather held more sway over daily life, even if you were just staying for a while. I already knew that if there were things I wanted to do outside, I'd better do them in the next few days. Rain alone rarely kept me from fishing, but this storm was going to bring arctic air along with it. I didn't want to be sitting in the canoe in a bone-chilling rainstorm. And even if I did, the fish certainly wouldn't be rising.

I still wanted to get some good-weather fishing in, but there would be plenty of time to do it on Tuesday or Wednesday. All things considered, there was only one thing to do—head up to Jim Whyte's cabin to spend the night.

Campsite Beneath the Stars

W hen I had packed for my trip to Onawa, I hadn't thought about overnight camping. After all, I thought I'd be spending all my nights at Uncle Roy's. But the weather forecast and Jim Whyte had changed my plans. The view of Borestone from Uncle Roy's porch was pretty special, but the perspective from Whyte's was spectacular. It explained in some part why he and Tessa hadn't wanted to leave very often. When I saw that view for the first time, I yearned to see what it would look like through the evening hours and deep into the night. Yet, while I wanted to treat myself to Jim Whyte's view, I didn't feel right about treating myself to his home. The one thing I shared with all those trespassers was the fact that I hadn't been invited in. But they had crossed the threshold and I hadn't, except with my eyes. I was set on keeping it that way.

When my parents and I had cleaned out Uncle Roy's, we had stashed all his camping gear in the spare bedroom closet. I gathered his old canvas pup tent, portable stove, stove fuel bottle, and cook set and took them out to my car.

A quick trip to the kitchen set me up with food from the icebox, a box of matches, and cooking utensils to accompany the folding knife and flashlight already in my pack.

I needed to scramble to make it up to Whyte's clearing before sundown. It was already midafternoon. I was in such a hurry that I got a mile up the road before I realized I'd left my sleeping bag behind. Going back to get it cost me another twenty minutes.

When I got to the trailhead, I opened the trunk, pulled out my backpack, and crammed everything inside. I was only going up to the cabin for the night, so there was no need to be too organized. It took longer to lash my sleeping bag and Uncle Roy's tent onto the outside than anything else.

I was glad I'd taken the trail before. As I hiked through the muddy section, the only footprints I saw were the ones I had left on the way down the day before. This section of trail wasn't seeing much action yet. It looked like I'd be the only person at the cabin, or for that matter, for miles around—just like Whyte had liked it.

I checked my watch when I entered the clearing: 5:07 p.m.

"One hour until sunset. Not bad," I said.

I hiked up through the clearing, set my pack on the porch, then leaned against the cabin to take in the view and wait for my breathing to return to normal. My back was soaked with sweat, and a single shiver prompted me to pull my sweater out of my pack to ward off the chill.

A bowl of soup would certainly hit the spot, I thought, so I began setting up what Uncle Roy called his "camper's stove" for the task.

Making the soup was a three-part symphony. Opening the soup can with the can opener on my pocket knife was the opening act. I didn't want to get the stove going and waste fuel while I worked the opener around the lip of the can at a painfully slow pace of an eighth of an inch at a time. Getting those blasted cans open without cutting your finger was always an achievement.

Once the lid was mostly cut, I carefully peeled it back to reveal the tomato soup concentrate inside. Now for the soup pot. Uncle Roy's camp pot set consisted of two pots and two lids, nested together, then secured with a leather strap and metal buckle. The cooking set had spent many days rolling around the bilge of a canoe, and though the pots hadn't suffered any effects, the buckle was pretty rusty and frustrating to deal with. Getting that buckle open and the stove lit were keeping me from chowing down, and I wasn't in the mood to fight with anything standing in my way.

I thought about cutting through the strap with my knife, but I finally prevailed. I took the lid off the larger pot so I could lift the smaller pot and lid out for making the soup. When I took the lid off the smaller pot, there was something inside. It was a piece of wax paper wrapped around something and secured with a rubber band. I unwrapped the object and saw that it was a red and black matchbook. I picked it up and flipped it around in my hand. The cover read "Hotel Robert Treat." White lettering on the black spine simply said "Newark, New Jersey."

It made sense that Uncle Roy would always carry matches in his cook set and that he'd taken care to try to keep them dry. What didn't make sense to me was where the matches had come from. There was no way Uncle Roy had ever gone to New Jersey. He often proudly declared that he had never left Maine in his lifetime. I don't think he ever even made it back to Portland after he left home for Onawa. I know he went to Bangor once to buy those canvas life jackets. Mom had said that might have been his first trip there, to which Dad had replied, "Knowing Roy, it was probably his last, too."

I opened the matchbook. Not a single match had been used. I didn't want to be the first. I set the matchbook on the porch and rummaged around my pack pocket until I found my stash of wooden matches. I drizzled a little stove fuel on the burner head, struck my match, and tossed it toward the stove.

With a whoomp, the fuel ignited with enough force to blow the match out. I loved it when that happened. The flame died down, and I turned the stove key to provide a steady flow of fuel. Now that a low blue flame was burning, I turned to the task of adding soup and water to the pot and setting it on the stove. Dinner would soon be served.

I picked up Uncle Roy's matchbook, looked at it again, and then wrapped it back up in the wax paper. It really wasn't worth me trying to figure out where Uncle Roy had gotten a matchbook, I thought. Roy may have lived alone and not traveled far in his life, but he hadn't been entirely cut off from the world. Maybe a person "from away" had left it at Randall's Store. Maybe one of his fishing buddies had left it at the cabin. And once he got the matchbook, he wasn't going to throw it away. Everyone who went through the Great Depression knew the value of keeping stuff.

I turned my attention to enjoying a pot of tomato soup and watching the twilight fade into night over Lake Onawa, Monson, and the great north woods of Maine.

After dinner, it was still light enough to stroll around the clearing. I climbed down from the porch and walked back behind the cabin. I knew the place had been dug over, and I wondered why. Much of the soil high on the ridge here was shallow. It had been almost exclusively created by hundreds of years of decaying logs and leaves. What hadn't been taken away by the wind gathered in the pockets between granite boulders. Then came pioneering mosses and ferns that allowed the soil to stabilize, then eventually deepen.

But here behind Jim Whyte's, something other than wind had sculpted the land. Many of the small boulders had been moved. You could see where they had been lifted out of the ground, then placed back in their holes, only not quite in the positions they had originally been in. It was clear that the marauders of Whyte's cabin hadn't been content with stealing almost everything left in the cabin—they literally left almost no stone unturned within a reasonable distance as well.

I thought I understood why. In 1930s Monson, like in many American communities, there were few jobs and plenty of despair. When someone died and left a cabin full of plates, books, linens, cookware, and Lord knows what else, it was an open invitation for everyone to help themselves. The tenor of the times didn't make their actions any less illegal, just a whole lot more understandable. In fact, the only thing I didn't understand about it was why Uncle Roy had never mentioned Jim Whyte or what went on here. I briefly wondered if he could even have been one of the townsfolk who came up here to pick through the cabin. Briefly enough to realize it was a ridiculous thought, that is.

Beyond the digging site, I noticed something I hadn't before. There were a couple of apple trees, which were being taken over by the forest. I imagined Whyte had enjoyed both the apples that grew from these trees and the deer that came to browse under them after some of the fruit had dropped to the ground.

It was getting too dark to stay behind the cabin much longer. I went back out front to enjoy the last of the twilight hour and set up the tent. There was no way I was going to sleep on the porch. Sleeping on wooden boards was pretty uncomfortable. I decided I'd much rather sleep on a forgiving patch of ground. The only problem was finding a flat spot in the clearing. Whyte's cabin was high on the knoll. Almost everything below it dropped steeply down toward the woods. I would have loved to set up the tent with the door facing due west—the same view I had from the porch—but the terrain wouldn't oblige. The best I could do was setting the tent on a flat spot just below the north corner of the porch so the door was facing the southeast corner of Lake Onawa.

There's nothing like the smell of a canvas tent. As soon as I unrolled Uncle Roy's old pup tent, the smell brought me back to the first time I was in it. My parents and I had been visiting Uncle Roy when I was ten. I was told a few years later that there had been fair discussion that evening about whether I was ready to spend my first night alone under the stars. Any fears they had of me being scared and running back to the safety of the cabin in the middle of the night were certainly unfounded. The only things I remembered about that evening were the novelty of sleeping in the tent and the unmistakable earthy smell of "well-seasoned" canvas. I slept through the whole night and deeper into the following morning than usual. My parents needn't have worried that living in the big city was going to diminish my inclination to be outdoors.

Uncle Roy's tent was nothing fancy. Like many basic pup tents of its day, it had no floor and no front door, a fact that caused no problem now that the mosquitoes were gone until spring. Besides, I'd have an unobstructed view.

I wished I could have slept as well in the tent as I had the first time around. Fact is, I slept horribly. After a few hours of flopping around, I gave up and decided to get out of the tent to stretch and look at the stars.

"Oh my gosh," I said. I had seen only a few nights when the stars were this bright, yet the view had never been this expansive. I took my sweater out of the tent and hopped up on the porch. I had taken my watch off when I went to bed, but I must have been on the porch for a good forty-five minutes looking at the stars and reveling in the quiet.

I was musing about going back into the tent when I was startled by a train whistle. It was from the eastbound Canadian Pacific train bound for St. John. I couldn't see the train's headlight at first, since it was obscured by trees. But I could hear the train moving across the landscape below, first down the far shore of Lake Onawa, then slowing to a few miles an hour as it approached the Onawa Trestle and inched its way across. Uncle Roy and I used to get a "canoe-eye view" of the westbound train during the late morning sometimes, so I knew the route. I closed my eyes and envisioned the train disappearing into the woods. I didn't open them again until the chug, chug, chug of train wheels had been rightfully replaced by the sounds of Big Wilson Stream and Little Wilson Stream tumbling over rocks way down in the valley. It was an incredible experience to be completely enveloped by nature's solitude. Even the trains didn't interrupt the tranquility of this place for long.

I reached back and patted the front wall of the cabin with my hand. "I know why you came here, Jim Whyte," I said. "And I also know why you didn't want to leave."

On Jim Whyte's Trail

The sky was just starting to lighten when I got out of the tent to make coffee. I used the last of the water from my canteens to make what Uncle Roy used to call "cowboy coffee," a fancy name for boiled water with grounds floating around in it. As he'd taught me, the key was letting the brewed coffee sit for a few minutes, then slowly pouring it until just before the grounds approached the lip of the pot.

As I spooned coffee into the pot, I wondered what Whyte had done for water. I doubted the likelihood of finding water high on the ridge. I hadn't seen any flowing water since I climbed up out of the valley. He had to haul it up here from down below, I thought. If so, maybe there was another side trail down from here. After breakfast, I set off to find it.

If there was another trail to and from the cabin, I thought it had to be on the north side. The trail I had taken here twice came in from the south and traversed the ridge. If there was another trail to the cabin, I would have seen where it joined mine.

I stashed everything except the tent inside of my pack. After the sun dried the morning dew off the canvas, I took the tent down, rolled it up, and lashed it to the outside. I hauled my pack up past the outhouse and stowed it under some bushes. It would be easier to move through the woods if I didn't have it on, and besides, if I did find Whyte's trail down to a water supply, I didn't want to have to climb back up hauling my pack. It would be easier to leave it on the ridgetop and reunite with it on my way back through.

I walked around to the north end of the clearing. A large log at the forest's edge grabbed my attention. It hadn't fallen down on its own. It had been felled with an axe. The cut wasn't recent. The wood had turned gray from several years' worth of snow, rain, and sun. I wondered why Whyte hadn't sawed it up for firewood until I saw it served another purpose. It obscured the existence of the trail behind it.

If this was the trail to Whyte's water source, why would he drop a log in front of it? There wasn't any plausible reason for making a difficult task any more so. Following the old trail through the spruce trees wasn't easy. The scrub growth was overtaking it. But as soon as I got into the hardwoods, I found a surprise. Not even twenty feet down from the ridge crest, a cleft in the granite exposed a flowing spring. Just below the source, someone had created a pool using nearby rocks. Deep and clear, this gathering spot undoubtedly made it easier to fill pails for hauling back to the cabin.

I cupped my hands in the pool and drew them to my mouth for a drink. I wished I had brought at least one of my canteens down with me. But I made do. Down past the pool, the water disappeared into a jumble of rocks before going underground again. I was certain that it reemerged farther downslope as it worked its way toward Lake Onawa.

Looking to my right as I faced down the mountain, I saw something unexpected—Whyte's trail continuing past the spring. Why would he have needed to climb down farther? One way to find out was to continue walking.

Through the hardwoods, the path was distinct, even years after Whyte had last set foot on it. The oaks and maples didn't grow fast enough to obscure the trail from the sides, but the yearly accumulations of leaves would eventually make it almost impossible to find. As I hiked down, I gained an appreciation for Whyte's genius. Unlike many trailblazers of his day, he hadn't made the trail head straight for the cabin from down below. Instead, he had cut zigzags called switchbacks into the slope to make ascents and descents easier.

Then it dawned on me. This wasn't an ancillary trail to Whyte's cabin. This was his primary route—the one he had used to haul stuff up from town on. Of course, he wouldn't have used the same route I came up, I thought. Between the mud and the long ridge traverse, it would have been a major task.

If this is Whyte's trail, I might be able to cross Big Wilson Stream on the bridge he built! I thought excitedly. As the trail took a sharp turn at the end of the ridge, I stopped for a few seconds, long enough to hear the rush of Big Wilson Stream.

Ten minutes later, I stood on the east bank. Jumbled steel cable and large planks were strewn along the embankment below me. Maybe the hardwoods hadn't been a match for Jim Whyte's trail, but Big Wilson Stream had dispensed with a key part of it in one spring melt. I didn't bother walking any farther. It wouldn't have been safe to attempt the stream crossing. The water was too high. Besides, I had already learned more than I thought I would on this trip to the cabin. It was time to climb back up, hoist my pack, and hike out.

On the way back to my car, I stopped to do something I hadn't in the rush to get to Whyte's cabin—spend a few minutes on top of Big Wilson Cliffs. Scarcely one-quarter mile from Jim Whyte's porch, this vantage point looked right down onto the town of Monson. The white steeple of the community church and the glimmer of Lake Hebron just west of town were unmistakable. Looking to the south, I couldn't see Uncle Roy's camp, but I could make out a little piece of the far end of Lake Onawa. I could even see a short section of train tracks and most of the trestle.

I could imagine Whyte scrambling up here to watch the few lights of the town come on as twilight settled over the valley. Someone had certainly spent evenings here. A ring of rocks bore the soot of several dozen campfires.

I took a final look toward the village, then made my way back down through spruce and into the golden and red maples that would surround me all the way back to my car. Enough leaves had fallen to make my walk noisy. The crunching undoubtedly scared the deer for miles around.

As I walked, I thought about how the Jim Whyte story was beginning to consume my vacation. I wondered if I had already gone too far, poking around his cabin, his clearing, his trail. Asking Tom and Lydia Randall about Whyte sure seemed like something I shouldn't have done, given how our talk had ended. And I certainly didn't know how to approach talking to Campbell about him or whether I should even try. Granted, I wasn't a complete stranger, but I was closer to being a stranger than a friend, especially since I hadn't shown up in Onawa for ten years.

I thought about taking Tom Randall with me to Campbell's, but that didn't seem right, either. I wondered if that would feel too much like an ambush. "Hey Phil, Tom Randall here told me you needed to tell me something that he couldn't. How 'bout it?"

No. That wouldn't do.

In the end, I decided there were only two paths to take—either let the story drop and spend the rest of the week fishing at Uncle Roy's, or drive up to Campbell's to see if he'd talk about Jim Whyte.

Whyte's Incredible Caper

Campbell leaned against his porch railing and gazed in the direction of Jim Whyte's cabin. I looked, too. All I could see was the spine of the ridge silhouetted against a backdrop of stars.

"Stories," said Campbell. "Every one of us has one. And they die along with us if we don't share them. Jim Whyte knew. That's why he told me so much toward the end."

He turned and looked back toward me perched on the front edge of the chair, still staring out. "But the thing he didn't know was that telling stories only buys you time—the stories only last as long as the people you tell them to can remember them, then they get covered up and lost forever, just like the trail to his cabin."

Campbell took a sip of scotch and looked down at the glass as if wondering whether he should take one more. He set it back down on the railing instead and turned back toward the view. He always seemed more comfortable speaking to everyone and no one at the same time, like when he was sitting behind me in the canoe.

"You know, I've often thought that the rumors about the hermit from Monson would fade. And I was right. If the Randalls and I didn't say anything, it wouldn't be long before nobody remembered Jim Whyte. Like you said when you got here, if Roy hadn't given you that hiking book, you wouldn't have come here to ask questions about him, either."

I hadn't moved since Campbell had started talking. I didn't dare. My butt hurt from perching on the front of the Adirondack chair, but

I wasn't going to so much as shift to one side until Campbell got through talking. I didn't know if I'd get him warmed up again.

He backed up a few feet and sat down next to me. But instead of sliding all the way back into the seat, he stayed perched on the front. I guess that made it easier for him to keep shuttling back and forth between the chair and the railing. Nonetheless, he kept looking out over the trees and talking as if I wasn't there.

"Of course, everyone in town wanted to know his story—at least the good parts, like what brought him to Onawa or how he learned how to build a cabin. But he wasn't about to share any of it. And thanks to the Randalls keeping their promise, you only know a little. Just up until when Tessa Whyte left town, is that what you said?"

"Yes, and I don't even know a whole lot about that," I said. "The Randalls seemed pretty intent on me talking to you, that's for sure."

Campbell tossed back the last of his scotch and water, then set the glass right where it came from—a ring of water on the table marked the spot. He was always aware of his actions. Maybe that's what made him such a great flycaster.

"You want another?" he asked as he reached for the bottle.

I didn't really want a refill, but I figured I'd better take one. I had come to get the story of Jim Whyte from the only living person who knew all of it and would share it with me. I nodded, and he dispensed another round.

With fresh drink in hand, he leaned back in his seat and put his feet up on the railing. Then he got quiet.

I had been afraid that this would happen from the time I decided to drive up to Campbell's cabin. The easy part of the conversation was over. That probably meant the whole conversation was over—just like when I was a kid at the dinner table. I started thinking about what I could say to make it sound like I was fine leaving things where they were, but Campbell spoke first.

"Jim Whyte stayed up in that cabin living the high life for more than twenty years. Then, just after Tessa left, something hit his finances hard," Campbell said. "Like most of us, Jim was able to shoot a few deer, and he had his orchard. But he was also getting older—I'd guess he was sixty then—and couldn't quite do what he used to. He was smart enough to know that he'd have to do something more than canning food and bagging a couple of deer to keep him eating through the Maine winter, even though Tessa was gone and there was only one mouth to feed. That's when he started selling stuff."

Campbell had brought out a cutting board with sausage and cheese on it before we sat down. He glanced at it briefly, then decided better of it.

"Lydia Randall says that a couple of years after Tessa left, Jim Whyte took a ride down to Greenville Junction to sell an emerald ring. She found out through a friend who worked at A.A. Craft's department store. Anyways, Jim found out that they paid cash for jewelry, so he showed up with a ring that he carried in a tin box. All he said was that he had picked it up in his travels and it was time to sell it. Lydia's friend never did say how much they paid. I guess there are limits to gossip, even in this neck of the woods. But whatever he got for that ring got him through the better part of the year. At least until October, when I saw the signal from Big Wilson Cliffs."

Campbell put a big chunk of sausage in his mouth, then pushed the cutting board toward me. My mother would have scolded me for not offering food to a guest first, but scarcity and solitude had helped forge other habits here at Campbell's cabin. I took a piece of cheese from the cutting board, popped it into my mouth, and turned away. I couldn't help but smile, hoping the fishing would be good at Uncle Roy's camp. It would be nice to eat something else for a change.

"It was two nights after I saw Whyte flashing his lantern when the train came back through from Montreal. I was ready. I had a feeling Whyte was going to meet it—that the signaling from the cliffs was setting up the rendezvous—so I walked down to the tracks to see if I was right. Around midnight, I found a spot upstream from Whyte's bridge, high on the bank and behind some boulders. It was the perfect place to wait. If I guessed right, Whyte would cross his plank bridge scarcely one hundred feet in front of me, turn downstream, climb the bank up to the train tracks, and head east toward the clearing that surrounds the tracks just before they cross the Onawa Trestle. The woods were way too thick and tight against the tracks anywhere else. I guess I could have just waited up by that spot, but I wanted to see him cross the bridge. That would leave no doubt that it was Whyte.

"About ten minutes before the 1:00 a.m. train from Montreal was due to come through, I saw something moving on the opposite bank. I crouched down as far as I could behind the boulders. My foot kicked out a rock behind me, but I didn't need to worry. You couldn't hear anything above the sound of the stream. The figure moved down onto the bridge. He used one hand to grab the cable railing. In the other, he carried a lantern. It was lit, but the shades were covering the sides, and there was just a hint of light coming out from behind them.

"I could tell from his stature and his gait that it was Jim Whyte. He was wearing a dark overcoat and that black sailor's cap he always wore when it was cold. He climbed the opposite bank on the trail, then disappeared over the top. I wanted to give him a head start down the rails, but not too much of one. We had about ten minutes before the train came through."

"You followed him?" I asked. "Weren't you worried about getting caught?"

"I figured there was no way in hell he thought anyone was there. The only people who could have seen his lantern two nights before were me and whoever he was signaling to on that train. The engineer would have been past the only clearing where he could have seen the signal. And the only reason the guy farther back on the train could have seen all three flashes of the light is because the train was slowing down as it approached the trestle. I doubt Whyte even considered that my porch gave the only other clear view to his cabin.

"Just the same, my heart was pounding when I got to the tracks. As I figured, Whyte was working his way down the rails. I knew that when that train whistle blew, he'd turn around. It's human instinct. All I needed to do was hide on the far side of the tracks before the whistle blew. And I made it by only a few seconds, I'll tell you.

"Damn, that train was loud! I dove into the spruce trees next to the tracks just before the engine rounded the bend and its headlight lit up everything in its path. Whyte was nowhere to be seen. Before the train started passing, I could see far enough down the tracks to know he was hiding, too.

"I covered my ears as the worst of the roar went by. By my recollection, there were fifteen cars on that freight train. As the train slowed for the trestle, the caboose passed by my hiding spot. I didn't dare move until it was well past me—at least one hundred yards.

"I crawled to the edge of the gravel and peered down the tracks. As the train slowed to go over the Onawa Trestle, someone opened the caboose door and came out to stand on the rear deck. He raised a lantern and flashed one red signal. Barely twenty feet behind it came a single flash of white from the edge of the woods. The figure on the caboose tossed something toward the place where the white light was, then went back inside the train, which hadn't stopped moving the whole time.

As the train disappeared into the night, I crawled back into the spruce trees and waited.

"Jim Whyte walked back up the tracks—right past where I was crouched. He was carrying the bundle in one hand and his lantern in the other. I might have been lying still, but my heart was throbbing like that time I slipped off the rocks and went over Big Wilson Falls with my fly rod. I waited a good fifteen minutes for him to get past me and back on his trail before I started making my way back here. When I got back, I sat by the fire and thought about what I had seen. Most of all, I wondered what was in that bundle. It didn't take much to figure it wasn't legal, but it wasn't the first time the guy was hiding something. Your Uncle Roy and I figured that out thirty-four years before. But that's a story for another day."

Campbell stood up and rubbed his beard for a few seconds, then set his empty scotch glass on the cutting board. I took the hint, placed my glass next to his on the board and stood up to leave.

"Supposed to be warm tomorrow," I said. "You want to come over to Uncle Roy's and do some fishing in the afternoon?"

"You mean, do I want to come over and talk about the hermit of Monson some more while we try to land some trout?" asked Campbell.

I didn't know whether he was being serious or sarcastic, so I didn't say anything. Campbell stood there holding the cutting board and glasses for a bit, then he set them back down. He walked back to the railing and stood facing me with his back against one of the support posts.

"Let me ask you something. How much time have you spent alone, Ben?"

The question took me by surprise. I hadn't given it much thought.

"More than most people, I suppose," I said. "I'm comfortable hiking, fishing, or hunting by myself, if that's what you mean. But I haven't spent any more than a few days by myself. Why do you ask?"

"Because people who spend a lot of time by themselves get judged by those who don't," Campbell said. "What most people don't understand is that being self-reliant is something you have to work your butt off to make happen. Every day you—and only you—decide what to do and how to do it. Everything—staying fed, staying warm and dry, staying healthy—depends on your mind and body. That's well and good if your mind and body are working right. But if you don't watch out, isolation can poison your mind. When there's nobody there to help set you straight, you can start believing and doing some really crazy stuff."

Campbell half turned and pointed toward Whyte's cabin. "Whatever else I tell you about Jim Whyte, know this. People have spun all sorts of wild stories about him because they didn't know him. But I did. I know what he did and why he did it."

I had hardly ever seen Campbell so worked up. He was normally even-keeled, except for the few times I'd heard him deliver a well-practiced hunting or fishing story. But this was different. He was defending Jim Whyte's reputation as if it were his own. It made me wonder if Campbell had ever been worried about losing his mind and whether Whyte had helped him somehow.

"How's two o'clock at Roy's sound?" Campbell asked. "And on two conditions. You're cooking dinner, and I'm on the road back here before dark."

"Done deal," I said.

Campfire Tales

The last time I went fishing with Uncle Roy, he thought I was still too young to fish from the bow. He was afraid I'd lose track of my back cast and snag his ear. Maybe he was right. I thought about that last paddle on the lake with him as I was preparing the canoe for Campbell's arrival. That day had been a lot like this one—with bright orange and yellow leaves framing the lake under as blue a sky as you could ever see. All we needed now was a bunch of brook trout to greet our casts.

I was glad that my parents hadn't put the canoe under the porch for winter storage yet. They had taken it out of the water but stored it upside down about ten feet inland with one end tied to a tree. I flipped the canoe over, checked it for cobwebs (I had gotten a mean spider bite on my foot one time), and dragged it across the lawn toward the water's edge. I wanted to be ready to get fishing as soon as Campbell arrived.

That plan went kaput as soon as I saw Tom Randall's delivery truck pulling into the clearing. Campbell's truck had made it as far as Randall's Store and then given up the ghost, so Tom had offered to give Campbell a ride. The two old friends were talking when they got out of the truck.

"I haven't been here since just after Roy died," said Tom. "Looks pretty much the same—that's a compliment!"

"Not bad, seeing as my folks don't get up here all too often," I said. "So, Tom, are you going fishing with us?"

"Nope. Lydia would have my head. I promised I'd drop Campbell off, help her finish the day at the store, then come back to get him at six thirty." Tom gestured toward my soon-to-be fishing partner. "You got enough to eat and drink for when I get back? I can bring something from the store if you need it."

"A few beers wouldn't hurt," I said. "Should have plenty of everything else, thank you."

Campbell slapped Tom on the back before he jumped into the truck and drove off.

"A 1940 Ford truck," Campbell said as Tom drove away. "Fine machine. Probably won't overheat all the time like mine." He walked over toward the dock and paused to look across the lake.

"Damn, this might be the best day of the whole year," said Campbell. "Warm enough to fish and cool enough to keep most of the bugs away. How 'bout you take the bow? Just watch your back cast."

To put it mildly, the fish didn't hold up their end of the bargain. We tried all the old reliable spots, five of them in all. We tried both dry files and wet. Whatever the fish were feeding on, we didn't seem to be finding the right combination. The last spot we tried casting in ended up being in the southeast corner of the lake near the Onawa Trestle.

"Can't see that trestle and section of tracks without thinking of Jim Whyte," said Campbell.

I didn't say anything or even turn around. He knew that I heard him. I simply lifted my dry fly off the surface, roll-cast it to a spot close to shore, and started stripping the line back to me about ten inches at a time. Uncle Roy had taught me that if I periodically created a little ripple on the surface with the fly, a fish might rise to take it.

"After I followed him to the railroad tracks that night, I didn't say anything to anyone—not even to your Uncle Roy. I just waited. I had a feeling whatever Whyte was up to would make him leave town.

"Three days after he picked up the package from the train, Jim Whyte came down from his cabin and walked into Tom Randall's store. He told Tom that he'd gotten word that his mother had taken ill, so he was going to catch the next train from Onawa and go to New York City to help her out. He said he'd be back in a week.

"When I went into town later that day to buy food, Tom told me about it. He knew I could keep a secret. He was worried that if people knew Whyte was gone for a week, they might beat a path up to his cabin—not to steal anything, but just because they were nosy."

Bam! A fish hit my fly and immediately started running. I tugged the line to set the hook, and the fight was on. Campbell was delighted.

"Big, fat brookie, I'll bet," he said. "I'll hand you the net."

Five minutes later, we saw the fish as I reeled him in toward the side of the canoe. It was so big it almost wouldn't fit in the net at all. Its coloring was gorgeous—it had a deep green back with bright red, yellow, and orange speckles of color on its sides and belly. In all the years I'd fished Lake Onawa, I'd never landed such a huge fish. It was a good sixteen inches long and at least two pounds.

I carefully removed the hook from the trout's mouth and prepared to reintroduce the fish to the lake, just like Uncle Roy had taught me.

"You're not going to keep it?"

Panicked wasn't exactly the right word, but there was some tension in Campbell's voice. The fish would have made a fine dinner. I knew that. But this fish was unlike any I had caught before in this lake.

"I think he earned the right to be left alone," I said. I slowly lowered him over the side. He was still tired from his unexpected ordeal. I gently moved him back and forth to move water and air through his gills, then he slipped out of my hands and dove down into the darkness. It was beautiful and right.

I rinsed my hands in the lake, then turned back toward Campbell. "Number 12 Adams," I said before he could ask. "I always catch fish on that pattern. It may take a while, but they always come home."

"Same with Jim Whyte," he said. "Exactly one week later, he was back from New York. And Tom Randall said the first thing he did was do some hefty stocking up on groceries. That was unusual. Back when Tessa was around, Whyte had been rolling in dough. He was even the first one in Monson to own a car. Bought it brand new, then cut a road partway up the back side of his mountain. Then he hit the skids. Things were so tight, he started selling things. And his swanky car just sat up on the hill alongside his cabin. He couldn't even afford to put gas in it. Now suddenly he was back to filling up his pantry with stuff from Randall's and taking road trips to Guilford and back."

"Feast or famine," I said.

"More than a feast," said Campbell. "But I wondered how long he could go before he'd need to signal the train again." Campbell hadn't cast his rod for a while. At first, he had been sitting with it across his lap, then he decided to place the reel end under his seat and the tip end into the bilge, signaling the end of his fishing day.

"What do you say we go back and eat?" he asked. It was really a formality because he had already picked up his paddle. "Tom will be meeting us soon, and he'll probably want to join us for a hamburger or two."

"Fine by me," I said. I had already had a successful afternoon. Everything else would be a bonus.

When we got back to Uncle Roy's dock, Tom Randall was there to help steady the canoe and haul our gear to solid ground.

"I brought that cold beer you asked for," said Tom. "Let's sit on Roy's porch for a bit."

The three of us sat overlooking the lake and Borestone. After telling Tom about the giant brook trout I landed, I leaned down to untie my soaking wet sneakers.

"One thing about canoes," said Campbell. "Your feet are always going to get wet. Doesn't matter if you get in and out of the canoe from the dock or not. The water from the paddles and the fly lines are the culprits."

His comment made me think of something. When I went into Uncle Roy's to fetch some dry socks and shoes, I also went to the pile of camping gear I'd stowed by the back door and grabbed something from the bottom of the pile.

"You guys remember this?" I asked after the screen door had slammed behind me, announcing my return to the porch.

Campbell laughed.

"Roy's pots and pans. Haven't seen those in a few years. He always used to take them in the canoe. He tied them to the thwart with a leash so he wouldn't lose them if the canoe flipped over. Every once in a great while, if the fishing wasn't good, he'd get me to paddle ashore so he could make a batch of coffee. I can still see him fumbling with that stove and stacking rocks to make a windscreen so the flame wouldn't blow out."

While Campbell was talking, I unbuckled the leather strap that held the pots together, removed the pot lids, and pulled out the wad of wax paper inside.

"The reason I ask," I said, "is because I found this the other day when I was camping up at Jim Whyte's cabin."

Campbell's eyes got big when he saw the red, white, and black matchbook cover. He glanced over at Tom, then back at his fingers.

"Hotel Robert Treat, Newark, New Jersey," he said. "I gave these matches to your uncle a long time ago. I'm surprised he kept them, being that he wasn't a fan of Jim Whyte."

Campbell handed the matchbook to Tom.

After handling it for a moment, Tom suddenly got really quiet. He just sat looking past the matchbook toward the worn floorboards at his feet. It seemed to me like something about that matchbook was bothering him, something Campbell also knew about. I waited for one of them to say something.

Finally, Tom looked up and out toward the lake. "I remember you telling me that it was quite the hotel," he said. I found it interesting that he didn't look toward his old friend as he spoke.

"It should have been for what they charged," said Campbell. "But I needed someplace to lay over for a night before catching the north-bound train, and that was it. I didn't take enough matchbooks to make up for the bill, but I took a big handful and didn't feel too guilty about it."

"What were you doing in New Jersey?" I asked. "I never knew you to want to leave Monson."

Campbell turned and looked at me. "I didn't want to leave. In fact, other than a couple of trips to Boston and one other, I'd never set foot outside of Maine." Campbell turned his gaze back toward Borestone and seemed to consider whether to say anything more. He slowly ran his hands fore and aft along the chair arms before he spoke, then said something that took me by complete surprise.

"But I needed to see Jim Whyte before he died."

More silence. It was my turn to get antsy. I had been raised not to ask many questions. I could hear Mom's voice telling me that if people wanted to share something, they would. I had already pushed it to ask Campbell what took him to New Jersey, and I had gotten away with it. But now the conversation was stuck again. The longer no one said anything, the more I wanted out.

"I'm going to start the fire. It will take a bit for it to make a good set of coals for our burgers," I said. I walked down off the porch and started collecting some sticks to use as kindling. It wasn't long before I heard Campbell and Tom speaking in low, monotone voices. I couldn't make out what they were saying. It was by their design, obviously. I supposed it was about Campbell's trip to New Jersey, but I would never know for certain. By the time I got back to the porch, they were chatty again.

"While you were gone, we got to talking about something," said Campbell. "Turns out that when I went to see Jim Whyte, I brought more than matchbooks back with me."

"I couldn't keep it quiet," said Tom. "And Campbell had every right to stay mad at me about it."

"But Whyte is gone, and those who remember him will be gone in a few years, too," said Campbell. "So, I told Tom I wasn't going to mention his slipup ever again—that if anyone ever asked him about it, he could go ahead and tell them what happened…if he wanted to, that is. This old misunderstanding has been sticking around like the smell of a dead mouse under the porch."

"That's one way of putting it, I guess," said Tom. "Well, Philip, seeing as Ben should probably know, go ahead and tell him what happened when you went to see Whyte. Then I can tell the rest. I'll go fetch another round of beers while you get started."

Campbell reached for the beer on the arm of his chair, took a healthy swig, and then set the bottle back down with the label facing him.

"In 1933, I got word that Whyte wasn't doing well. His second stroke had really made him weak. He was seventy-five years old by then and didn't have much fight left in him. So, I caught the train from Onawa station and headed south as Whyte had done so many times before me. Except instead of going to New York City, I continued south to a town called Burlington, New Jersey."

"Never heard of it," I said.

"Neither had I. It's down by Newark. There was a home run by the Freemasons down there, and they took him in. When I got there, I was met by a frail shadow of the man who had lived on the ridgetop. He was damn happy to see me, even though he couldn't say it—the stroke had taken his voice away. But his eyes teared up, and his mannerisms were full of gratitude. He still had one good arm—his left—and he would squeeze my forearm for emphasis. We couldn't communicate well. It was more me asking questions and him nodding, really. I would say something like 'Onawa' or 'Randall's Store' and he would nod affirmatively and so forth. I stayed there for about three hours. He didn't want me to leave, but the staff did. I think those nurses thought it was too much strain on him."

Campbell paused long enough to reach for the bottle opener and fresh beer Tom handed to him and set them down on the left arm of his chair.

"Just as I was getting ready to leave, Jim Whyte stood up and walked over to the spare bed—there were two twin beds in his room. The one he walked to was never used. It was all made up with a white bedspread on top. He took his finger and traced the number 40,000 on the bedspread, pointed down at the ground, and nodded yes to get me to understand. I nodded yes back to him. He wasn't going to let me leave until he was sure I understood what he meant. He grabbed my arm and gestured to the bedspread one more time. And again, I nodded yes. About then, the nurses showed up again to prompt me to leave. I shook Jim Whyte's remaining usable hand and said goodbye. That was the spring of 1933."

Campbell turned to his beer, and Tom picked up the story.

"I knew something was afoot when Campbell came in to buy some film and asked if he could borrow my camera," said Tom. "He had always made fun of mine, saying that cameras were only good for tourists. When I asked him why he had finally come around to the idea, he said he wanted to take some photos around Jim Whyte's cabin."

"Being honest. My first mistake," said Campbell. "My second mistake was telling Tom that Whyte had buried $40,000. My idea was to take the pictures back to New Jersey and have Whyte show me where the money was."

"But it poured the next day, and Campbell didn't go up there. Wouldn't have mattered anyway. The day after that, we got the news that Jim Whyte had died," said Tom.

"It's sad," said Campbell. "When the old man got on the train for New Jersey in 1932, it only took the crooks one day to steal everything Jim Whyte owned. The only thing left in the cabin was the beastly cookstove. They even took the painting of the guy's mother with them. It was a horrible thing to do, even during the Great Depression when people had nothing. Of course, there were rumors about who the thieves were, but that's all there ever was, just rumors."

"But it got worse when I let one person find out about the $40,000," said Tom. "I think every square inch of that mountain got dug up in a week. Even Jim Whyte's daughter showed up from New York with two men to do some digging up there. They kicked everyone out. Claimed it was their money and their right. But they left after two weeks and nobody ever found the money, if it ever existed at all."

"Oh, it existed," said Campbell. "He wouldn't have been so insistent about me getting the message."

"Well, no one will ever find it," said Tom. "It's been close to fifteen years."

Campbell nodded out toward the fire. "We're not going to have any decent coals unless you go feed that fire. Let's move down there so we have a chance of eating tonight."

As we got up and moved to the fire ring, I tried to process every-thing I'd just heard. How did Jim Whyte ever get $40,000? Where would he have buried it? And what about his daughter who had sud-denly shown up? I didn't know he even had a daughter. The longer I stayed around Onawa, and the longer I hung around with Campbell and Tom Randall, the more tangled the mystery became. And of course, we hadn't even gotten to Uncle Roy's role in the story. With only four days left until I had to be on my way back to Portland, I wondered how much more I'd have time to learn. But it seemed like the less I prodded, the more was revealed.

I asked the two old hands if they would tend the fire while I went inside to make the burgers. Uncle Roy had two folding grill gizmos with long metal handles. To use them, you'd make burger patties, set them on one side, then fold the other side over the top, sandwiching the burgers in between. The idea was that you'd position the grill over the coals, then flip it when one side of the burgers was done. I brought the burger-filled baskets out to the fire, handed them to Tom, and went back inside to get the buns, ketchup, and mustard. Tom was delighted.

"I think I sold these to Roy twenty years ago!" he said. "Bring a towel out, would you, so I don't burn my hands on the handles?"

Getting the burgers to grill without burning up was always a chal-lenge—too much of one to allow conversation to sidetrack the produc-tion. Tom was able to orchestrate tasty results. The buns didn't even get charred. I wasn't sure how he did it. I knew from my own experience that if I was lucky enough to get the burgers right, I wasn't going to push my luck with trying to toast the buns.

While Tom prepared the burgers and buns, Campbell and I moved the Adirondack chairs from the porch to the fire. It was starting to feel like October, and the fire would let us sit comfortably outside, at least until my guests climbed back into Tom's car.

When the burgers were gone and Campbell handed out the next to the last round of beers, he got back to the story.

"Well, we haven't much time before we need to go," he said. "What do you say we talk about the wives?"

Tom was leaning in toward the fire, and I could see his grin. "Yes, the wives. Not much to talk about with the first one," he said. "She was only here a year."

"Dora was her name," said Campbell. "He introduced her as his wife, didn't he, Tom?"

"Sure did. He showed up at the store showing off his wife, Dora, and his deed to thirty acres between Big Wilson Stream and Little Wilson Stream. He and Dora had arrived on the Onawa train and had come to the store to buy a few things. I remember she was a brunette. Small of stature. Much smaller than Whyte, and he wasn't a big man. He went about five foot nine or so. But I saw her fewer than a handful of times. She didn't even stop by the store on her way out of town the following year. As time goes by, I remember less about her. I'd probably have a hard time picking her out of a crowd, other than the fact she may have been the only four-foot-ten person there."

"Tessa was different," said Campbell. "For one thing, she stuck around."

Tom laughed. "Yeah. She lasted twenty times longer than Dora. I guess she was cut out for the hermit life."

"She was until she wasn't," said Campbell. "She was some pretty, though."

"Indeed," said Tom. "Tall with light brown hair that went down to the small of her back if it wasn't pinned up, which it usually was. She loved living up on that hill with Jim Whyte and working her fingers to the bone to make a go of it."

"They worked hard, but they also had help," said Campbell. "Whyte's mother had money. So did he—until it ran out. But Tessa left before that happened. It wasn't like she left because he went broke. Not at all. She left for some other reason. But on the flip side, I know that Jim Whyte loved that woman until the day he died and never loved anyone more."

"That was her last name," said Tom. "When you said the word *more*, it all came back. Her name was Tessa Mooers. It's an old Maine name. Word was she came from Milo."

"She *was* from Milo," said Campbell. "Scarcely forty miles from here. But after she left on Jim Melcher's bread truck, it's likely no one in this town saw her again. Jim Whyte certainly didn't. He told me to my face."

"Is she still alive?" I asked.

"Could be," Campbell said. "She was 'bout fifteen years younger than him, so that would make her about my age—seventy-ish. But don't you go chasing her down. I'm sure she'd want to be left alone. At this age, we all do."

"Not all of us," said Tom.

"Am I wrong, or was it less than a week ago you told me you were thinking of selling the store because you were getting tired of it?" asked Campbell.

"That had nothing to do with the customers. It's just getting harder to do everything we need to run the place," said Tom.

"Oh, I see," said Campbell. He was standing too far from the fire for us to see his face, but the tone of his comment was heavy with what we Mainers knew as Down East sarcasm.

"Well, on that note, I guess we should head back to the store to see if your car will start. If not, I'll drop you off at your camp," said Tom. "Ben, there are three beers left. I assume there's enough room in Roy's icebox for 'em."

"There's even ice left in the icehouse," I said. "Mid-October. I think that's a record to be hauling chunks of ice out of there, but it doesn't really count because no one was living here full-time to use it up like there was when Uncle Roy was here."

"Your folks paid me to fill the icehouse last February," Campbell said. "I guess they thought they'd get up here more than they did this summer, but you probably know more about that. 'Course I'm too old to cut and haul ice. I hired a few boys to do it and watched over the proceedings."

"They never said anything to me about it. But I don't live at home anymore, so these days that kind of thing only comes up in passing," I said.

The men bid me goodnight and walked across the lawn to reach the dirt driveway. After the truck doors slammed and lights from Tom's car swept across the lawn long enough for me to wave goodbye, I stood looking at the embers of the fire. Soon enough, the sound of Tom's truck wending its way up Uncle Roy's camp road disappeared. It was so still that the only sound was coming from the flames working on the piece of driftwood I had thrown onto the coals when the burgers were served.

A light breeze kicked up. It wasn't enough to blow any embers out of the fire ring, but it did make me turn up my collar and edge closer to the heat. If the wind started blowing any harder, I'd need to douse the flames. I rummaged around under the porch to find Uncle Roy's water pails, which were, thankfully, in their traditional spot and ready for action. I left an empty one next to the fire on my way to the lake to fill the other.

Back at the fire, the flames were behaving. I pulled a chair closer to the ring and sat perched on the edge, mesmerized by the patterns of the flames and embers. This was probably the last time I'd have the luxury of sitting outside by a fire at least until next spring. The rain was on its way, and the arctic winter winds and snows wouldn't be far behind. I looked at the empty Adirondack chairs to either side of me. Damn, I thought. I should have asked Campbell and Tom to help me carry them back to the porch. Those things were heavy as all get-out. I couldn't leave them out all winter, and Campbell would only be back by himself after I left on Sunday. Oh well. I'd have to drag 'em across the lawn and up the steps. No choice, really. But I didn't want to deal with them right then. The rain wasn't supposed to arrive until morning.

I raised my eyes from the fire long enough to gaze out toward the lake. "Funny how I came up here to spend all week fishing and I only got out in the canoe once," I said aloud. It struck me that I rarely spoke aloud unless I was here in Onawa. Most times it had been when I was in the canoe by myself. But this week, I also found myself doing it on dry land. It made me wonder if Campbell walked around his place muttering to himself, which made me laugh aloud. I could picture that. He was probably doing it this minute—sitting on the porch grousing about his truck, whether it started and got him home or not.

I stared back at the fire and began thinking about everything I'd learned about Jim Whyte over the last several days, and about Tom Randall and Phil Campbell, for that matter. I suddenly realized that I needed to write it all down. I ran into the cabin, pulled my notebook and pencil out of my daypack, and returned to the fireside. I chucked my notebook on the center chair, then went to the woodpile to fetch a few medium-size pieces of driftwood, enough to cast new light on my writing. There on the shores of Lake Onawa, almost within sight of Jim Whyte's cabin, I began documenting everything that I had heard that day—Campbell's account of Jim Whyte leaving for New York within days of the train passing through and how he returned to Monson flush with cash, the rift between Campbell and Tom Randall, the buried treasure that nobody ever found, Jim Whyte's mysterious wives, and Campbell's trip to New Jersey.

When I finished writing, I closed the notebook, tossed it on the chair Campbell had sat in earlier, and returned to my fire-gazing ritual. I looked at my watch. I had spent over an hour and a half writing notes, and I began wondering why I had felt so compelled to do it. Maybe it had to do with what Campbell had said on his porch, the idea that everyone had a story to tell that died with the last people who could remember it.

It was getting too cold to stay out by the fire unless I built it up again. I sat for just a few lingering minutes looking across the lake at the profile of Borestone. Clouds were moving in above the spruce-topped cliffs and beginning to block out the stars. I knew I had better get to sleep if I was going to beat the morning rain to the Adirondack chairs. I poured the water onto the embers, stirred the coals with a stick, grabbed my notebook, and headed inside to call it a night.

Restless for Answers

The bed in Uncle Roy's cabin was ancient. Like so many of his generation, he thought that the cure for a saggy mattress wasn't getting a new one, it was shoving boards between it and the huge metal springs beneath. That may have worked for a while, but no longer. At 3:00 a.m., I gave up and dragged the mattress onto the floor. At least this way there'd be some support under my back. Because I had stayed so long by the outdoor fire, I hadn't bothered to start a fire in the camp stove. And while I couldn't quite see my breath, it was cold and damp enough in the cabin to make me snuggle deeply down into my sleeping bag for another round of sleep.

When I awoke for good, it was still dark. I lit the kerosene lamp on the bedside table, then made a beeline for the woodstove. One of the unwritten family laws was to always leave the camp stove ready to light. It was a courtesy that came in handy in times like this. Hunting for newspaper, kindling, and firewood upon arrival at a cold camp is an inconvenience that can be avoided with some forethought. When I cracked open the stove door, I was happy to see that Dad had done his duty. I lit a match, tossed it in, and the fire started roaring. The stove always had a powerful draft. We always joked that we could throw a piece of petrified wood in it and it would still burn.

I held my hands above the stove's surface and rubbed them together. It wasn't long before I could feel the heat from below. I opened the door, placed another piece of wood over the growing flames, and then set off to get Uncle Roy's portable stove. Even though the woodstove was efficient, it would still take a good hour to bring my coffee water to a boil. Uncle Roy's "camper's stove" would do it in a fraction of the time, something I needed if I was going to get those chairs onto the porch before it rained.

I threw another couple of logs on the fire and went outside. The morning now gave me just enough light to work with. On my way outside, I stopped to put on the pair of Uncle Roy's deerskin work gloves that had hung on a nail by the porch door ever since I could remember. He'd be glad I was putting them to good use. I pulled two planks from under the porch and placed them over the steps to use as ramps. Then I took a deep breath and walked down to the chairs. Rather than drag them, I decided to crab-walk them over to the ramp, then haul them up front first. It was easier than I thought. Just as I got the last chair under the roof, the rain began. It was a heavy mist at first, then became steady. I stood and watched it for a few moments, then retreated to the warmth of the woodstove where I could prepare fried eggs and toast.

After breakfast, I sat next to the stove for a while, happy to be sheltered from the cold, soaking wet day of the world outside. This camp held so many memories for me. I had learned to swim at the end of Uncle Roy's dock. I had caught my first fish here—on two different kinds of fishing rods, no less. Most important, I had learned that nature's pace was the one that made me feel most at ease. It was why I had wanted to come and spend the week here.

I gazed at the log walls and rafters. Every log had been cut and set in place by Uncle Roy when he settled here in the 1880s. He stayed until the demands of staying here did him in. I never saw that as a bad thing. After all, he lived the life he wanted and died the same way. He also left our family with both this hand-built cabin and all the memories that were created within it—stories that would become family lore for generations. More than that, he gave me something that I would always carry within—the feelings of self-reliance and confidence that come from spending time outdoors.

The more I thought about Uncle Roy, the more I couldn't help thinking about his neighbor on the far ridge—a man who had also staked his claim, built his cabin, and stayed until the rigors of life did him in. But there were no work gloves hanging in Jim Whyte's cabin. There was no legacy left in those walls other than the marks left by an axe and a drawing knife. And, as far as I could tell, there was no family left to carry the memories of living with him. All that was left were the uninformed rumors of a few treasure-hunters and the truths known by Tom and Lydia Randall and Phil Campbell.

It was funny how my whole week had been taken over by Jim Whyte. I thought about the comment Campbell had made about people who spent a lot of time alone losing their minds. I also wondered if I was spending too much time poking into someone else's business. I guess Mom and Dad had done a good job of reinforcing that idea. But no matter what else I thought about, I kept coming back to the dismissive remark Uncle Roy had made about Jim Whyte that day when we were hiking up Borestone to go fishing. It seemed likely that Campbell had told him about Whyte getting a package thrown to him from the train. And since Uncle Roy had been a track inspector, maybe he got upset. On the other hand, in places like Onawa, small indiscretions were almost always forgiven. If nobody got hurt, most people looked the other way. After all, everyone was doing their best to get by. But there were limits. The ransacking of Whyte's cabin was certainly something that should have bothered anyone with a conscience as being beyond the pale. All told, it hardly seemed to me that whatever Jim Whyte was up to was worth getting angry about. But only Campbell could say for sure. And I wondered how much he would share.

Fifteen years ago, when we spent all those days fishing together, he had been livelier—telling funny stories and laughing more. These days Campbell still liked to talk, but he was a lot more careful about what he said. More deliberate. Maybe it was because he was getting to the age where Uncle Roy and Jim Whyte had died and he was thinking more about what was important. If that was so, wouldn't he want to make sure somebody knew the truth about the hermit before all that remained were whispers and rumors blowing over the lakes and ridgetops? It was curious that last night, after so many years of chiding Tom Randall for his slipup about the $40,000, that he decided to call a truce. I wondered if he'd be ready to talk about Uncle Roy's disdain for Whyte. If not that, maybe I could find out more about the hermit from Monson before I had to leave in four days.

The rain let up for a few minutes. There wasn't much to do that day other than read by the fire, but I didn't feel like it. Instead, I decided I might as well see if Campbell's car was still at Randall's Store and see where the day led me from there.

An Unsettling Discovery

The road to Monson was already a mess, and we hadn't seen the worst of the coming storm yet. Potholes and washouts kept me weaving my way along at five miles per hour. The roads would only get worse, and my car wasn't in great condition for taking them on. I'd bought the 1938 Ford Tudor—against Dad's better judgment—for $250. It had been just reliable enough to take me around greater Portland, but the only thing that set anyone's mind at ease about me taking it to Onawa was that if my car broke down somewhere, I could catch a train. I had thought about taking the train anyway, but I wanted to be able to drive around at least a little to see if Monson had changed at all. I could hardly have expected how much driving I'd end up doing when I got there.

Now I was doing my best to avoid puddles. The car always gave me trouble when the spark plug wires got wet. If I could just get to Randall's, then to Campbell's, I'd be okay. I had three and a half days to dry the wires out and get back on the road. I supposed I should have listened to Dad and saved up for some new wires, but I'd spent my money on dry flies instead. At least that number 12 Adams was worth the price. I'd caught a two-pound brookie on it!

When I made the bouncing twenty miles over the camp road and turned onto the main drag, I was some relieved. The roads would be in better shape for most of my remaining drive. My second wave of relief came when I saw that Campbell's truck wasn't parked at Randall's. I figured the coffeepot would be on, so I stopped anyway.

When the brass bell on the door announced my arrival, Lydia looked up from behind the counter.

"Well, I didn't expect to see you here today. Tom told me you were thinking of hunkering down at Roy's for a few days," she said.

"I was, but I decided to go see Campbell instead."

"Seems you two have a lot to talk about between reminiscing about Jim Whyte, your Uncle Roy, and all."

Well, apparently Tom had filled her in on everything we had talked about. I wasn't surprised. The lifting of the gag order on Tom's slipup was a pretty big deal.

"Where's Tom?" I asked.

"He's out back throwing a tarp over the woodpile. The forecast keeps getting worse. Now they're calling for two inches of rain," she said. "Why, do you need him for something?"

"Not really." I glanced around the store to make sure we were alone.

"There's no one else in the store. What's up, Ben?" she asked.

"I've been wondering about Tessa Whyte and why she left. Do you think she'd had enough of living up there as the wife of a hermit?" I asked.

"Nope. I think she still loved Jim," she said. "I just don't think she could spend all of her time with him anymore. I don't care how compatible a couple is. Spending all of your time together will kill a marriage. Why do you think I take shopping trips to Skowhegan? If Tom and I spent all of our time in this store or together at home, we'd drive each other crazy. My guess is she wanted to get a fresh start somewhere."

"So, after she left, Jim Whyte stayed around his cabin and never came to town except to shop? How did he do it? From the sounds of it, he never held a steady job."

"If Campbell wants to tell you, you'd better hear it straight from him. There are too many wild rumors about that," she said.

Tom had been outside since I arrived, and I was starting to feel guilty about it. "Do you think I should run out and give Tom a hand with that tarp?" I asked.

"I wouldn't bother. He's likely done by now. Do you want something to eat or drink?"

"Coffee, please," I said.

Lydia turned to pour a mug of coffee for me. She hadn't changed a lot over the twenty-five years I'd known her—or more accurately, remembered knowing her. I'd been told many times that the first time I visited Randall's Store I was barely a month old. Now in her seventies, Lydia was still sharp as ever. Tom may have been skeptical about her know-ing from the beginning that there was more to Jim Whyte than he was willing to share, but I wasn't. Over the years, I came to feel that Lydia Randall was something of a kindred spirit. While Tom paid attention to getting the big tasks done around the store, Lydia kept her focus on the people that came into it. It wasn't lost on me that the two smallest people I knew, Mom and Lydia Randall, were the two with the biggest hearts. Tom Randall may have been able to keep the store running by himself, but it was Lydia who was its steady, caring presence. She knew more about what was going on in Monson than anyone—not because she was nosey, but because she cared.

As Lydia poured my coffee, I noticed something I hadn't before. Her hands were shaking so steadily that the coffee was almost spilling out of my mug. Without turning around, she started talking to me.

"Go ahead and sit at the table. I'll bring your coffee over," she said.

I felt bad that she was self-conscious about the shaking, but I didn't think saying anything would help. She set the mug along with a spoon, a pitcher of cream, and a napkin on a tray, then brought them to me.

"Will you join me for a cup?" I asked.

"Why not?" she said. "Pretty slow morning here, anyway. People are staying inside."

The back door to the store flew open, and Tom appeared. "Damn door almost blew out of my hands," he said. "That blasted wind is crazy today."

He hung his hat on a nail, peeled off his rain slicker, poured a cup of coffee, and joined us at the table.

"Guess I earned a little break," he said. "Hand me the cream, Ben, would ya?"

"Gladly."

"Ben, how old are you?" he asked.

"Twenty-seven. Why do you ask?" I said.

"Have your parents ever told you about the Onawa train wreck?" Tom asked.

Lydia threw her upper body away from the table in surprise. "Tom Randall, don't you think that it's up to Ben's parents to decide whether to talk about that?" she said. "Why in the world are you bringing that up?"

"Because it has everything to do with what Ben's been asking us about since he got here." Tom looked at me again and waited for my answer.

"Never heard of it," I said.

"It's important for you to know what happened because practically everyone in the area was affected by it. No one more than your Uncle Roy."

"Uncle Roy? How?"

"Your parents were probably afraid that you were going to ask Roy about it if they told you when you were young. Then they may have figured there was no use telling you after Roy was gone. But if you spend time up here, you really need to know what happened," said Tom.

"First of all, it wasn't his fault," said Lydia. "It was a mistake. Any one of us could have made the same one."

I didn't know what to say. I went numb and looked straight ahead at one of the coffee stains on the blue tablecloth.

"It happened the week before Christmas, 1919, the winter after you were born, as it turns out," said Tom. "I unlocked the store for the day and was just getting the woodstove going when I heard the crash. A few seconds later, a couple of guys on their way to the slate works ran in and said that two trains had collided just west of the Onawa station and there were bodies everywhere."

"It was horrible," said Lydia. "Doctor Clancy rushed over there. We sent all the bandages and towels we had to the scene. But we decided we needed to stay here and open in case anyone needed anything."

"There had been one eastbound freight train and four westbound passenger trains," said Tom. "The freight train was coming from Megantic, and the four westbound trains were carrying passengers from an ocean liner that had docked in St. John, New Brunswick, the day before. The guys on the freight train were hauling twenty-six cars and working their way east. They had let two of the four passenger trains pass them at different sidings. Everything was going as planned."

Tom looked at his coffee mug for a moment, decided the better of taking a sip, and took a deep breath instead.

"The freight train was stopped at the Morkill siding waiting for orders. Soon they got word from the switchyard. The operator told them that 'the third Train 39 was late, and the fourth Train 39 was eight hours late.' But they misunderstood. They thought both trains were running eight hours late."

He paused for a few seconds and looked toward Lydia. "After the fact, Lydia and I wondered why they didn't give each of those trains a different number," he said.

"I guess it made sense to the railroad that every train that set out from the luxury liner should have the same route number or something,"

Lydia said. "But looking back on it, they must have realized it fed into why the men on the freight train got confused."

"Anyway," said Tom, "those poor men on the freight run made a dash for Brownville Junction, thinking that they would get there well before the passenger train. The trains collided head-on at full speed at a bend in the track just west of Borestone. The wreckage was everywhere. The engineer and conductor on the freight train were killed. Twenty-four people on the passenger train died, and another fifty were injured."

"The wooden cars of the passenger train even caught on fire. You could see the smoke from everywhere," said Lydia.

"But how was Uncle Roy involved?" I asked.

"He was the guy who issued the orders to the freight train that morning," said Tom. "He never forgave himself for the accident. Even though the engineer misheard what he said, Roy always felt that if he had been clearer, all those people would have been saved."

I was stunned. Just a few hours before, I had been reveling in my happy family history under Uncle Roy's roof. Now this.

"I can't believe it. Uncle Roy never said a word."

"I figured he didn't," said Tom. "He was so ashamed. It took Roy quite a while to recover from it, even though the railroad bosses and the other guys on the crew were behind him. They wanted him to stay in the switchyard, but he refused. I think he would have left work for good and stayed in his cabin until he died if he hadn't needed the money. But the track inspector job let him stay employed and enjoy plenty of time to himself—almost all of it, really. I guess it worked out as best it could."

"The whole thing was so terrible," said Lydia. "I wish you could have known Roy before those days. He was so full of life. He was always a joy to see. He'd come by the store after work and swap fishing stories with Tom and anyone who came in to buy something, whether they were from here or just passing through. But after the accident, he would barely stay longer than it took to buy his beer and groceries and leave. He was nice and all, especially to us, but he was different. Beaten down, I guess you'd call it."

"He got a little better as the years passed," said Tom. "There were times when he, Campbell, and I would go fishing, and he'd show glimpses of the old Roy. Of course, we'd always have to fish at his place. He never wanted to come over to Lake Hebron, even if Lydia offered to cook dinner, and he barely came into town anymore. His whole life was his job and his cabin. I guess it's the way he decided he needed to be."

"He would get excited when your parents came to visit. Especially after you came along and got old enough to go fishing with him," said Lydia. "When he loaded up with groceries, we knew the Harmons were coming up to visit and we wouldn't see Roy again until you left and he went back to work."

"He sure hid everything well. He always seemed like he was enjoying himself when we were here," I said.

"That's because he didn't have to worry about people talking about him after he passed them on the street," said Lydia. "Whether it was true or not didn't matter. Roy made it so. That's the part I couldn't understand. He really tortured himself, especially those first few years. All he did was walk the tracks, stop at the store, and go back to his cabin. I wonder why he didn't move away. For the longest time, I feared he might do himself in. Then I just prayed he would find peace with what had happened. I felt so relieved after Tom visited him the week before Roy died."

"He hadn't stopped by the store for a few days, so I wanted to make sure he was okay," said Tom. "Roy was standing out front, leaning on a shovel handle and looking at Borestone when I drove in. I had brought some eggs, bread, and beer from the store—a sort of care package. When he saw it, he smiled and said, 'I'm not laid up, Tom. Just took a few days off to get ready for winter. I appreciate the gesture, though.'

"At first, he wasn't going to let me help him, although he didn't bark too much about me helping him stow the canoe under the porch. After we were done, we sat out front and cracked open a few beers. It was about this time of year. The leaves on those birch trees by the shore had turned that bright yellow color they only show for a couple days.

"After gazing around for a time, Roy said, 'I'm going to miss this place.' It took me by surprise, and I tried to make a joke about it, but Roy just kept looking out at the lake. He said that he would never get over the fact that he'd made one big mistake that cost a lot of people their lives.

"The way he was talking was making me uncomfortable. 'Don't look scared, Tom. I'm not going to kill myself,' he said. 'I'm just stating the facts. This place helped me come to peace with what happened. I made a mistake. A terrible mistake. And lots of people forgave me for it. But I didn't feel that I deserved their forgiveness…or even that it was theirs to give. Let me tell you, it took years of sitting out here—replaying that day in my head, wishing to God it never happened, wondering why something didn't keep me from going to work that day, wishing I could have gone to Scotland and England to tell every family that lost someone that day that I was sorry. I sat through thousands of sunrises and sunsets sorting through it all. That's what it took for me to get to the place where I forgave myself.'

"'Well, I'm glad you got there, Roy,' I said. 'I'd be lying if I thought you would after all these years.' Roy said, 'As much as I hate to admit it, Tom, I also came to realize that I could have gotten there faster if I had asked for more help.'"

Tom turned his coffee cup around and around in his hands, then looked up at me. "It was kind of awkward talking about it," he said. "I was raised to keep personal stuff to myself. I'm sure Roy was, too. I even feel odd talking about it now. But I was afraid that if you found out about the accident someday, you'd never know that Roy had come to terms with it before he died."

Lydia hadn't said anything for a while. She'd been shifting glances between Tom and me to get a read on how things were going. I guess she figured things were safe, because she got up to make another pot of coffee.

"I wish I had stayed and talked to Roy more that day at his cabin," said Tom. "He only lived another week. The tough part for me was that he stopped by the store one day and actually stayed a bit to talk, just like the old days. But I needed to get to the bank before it closed, so I couldn't. I thought we'd get another chance, but we didn't.

"I played that conversation I had at the lake with Roy over and over in my mind. I came to realize that what he meant was that Campbell, you, and your parents were part of the help that got him to his place of peace. That a man can get beaten down if he has nothing to look forward to, especially if his past and present are always framed by a tragedy.

"When you were up here, it gave Roy a chance to focus on something else—sitting in the canoe with you and sharing what he knew about fly-fishing. It doesn't seem like much to most people, I suppose, but I know it helped him carry his head just a little higher. He'd be really glad that you're up here living in his cabin, Ben, even if it is just for ten days."

"I appreciate that, Tom. And everything you told me this morning. I had no idea," I said.

"Well, like I said, I'd rather have you get the story from me than from someone who doesn't know what they're talking about."

I was really disappointed in my parents. Why hadn't they shared the story of the train wreck with me? Even if they had been trying to protect my opinion of Uncle Roy, it didn't make sense. Didn't they think it was going to come out someday? Maybe they just prayed I would stay at Roy's and not go into town at all. It seemed pretty desperate to believe I'd never find out about it. Then again, it was just like my dad to keep things off-limits for discussion. Maybe that's why I wanted to be a reporter so much. The only thing better than learning how to ask questions without feeling guilty about them would be writing stories using what I'd learned.

Lydia came back to the table with a fresh pot of coffee and more cream for Tom. I glanced out the front window. The rain was pouring off the awning in sheets. Thinking about my spark plug wires, I thought the better of leaving for Campbell's just yet.

"Thank you. I'll have one more," I said. "So, those years right after the accident must have been interesting up this way. You really had two hermits in town. Jim Whyte and Uncle Roy."

"Three, really, if you consider Campbell," said Lydia. "When your uncle went off to be by himself, Campbell lost his best friend for a while."

"A year and a half, at least," said Tom. "The second spring after the wreck, when the ice was off Lake Onawa, Campbell showed up at Roy's with his fly rod and a box full of streamer flies he had tied over the winter. He told Roy that he wasn't leaving until they sat in the canoe and cast their lines for a few hours. The way Campbell tells it, neither one of them said anything the whole time. But Campbell still calls it the year that two things thawed out—the lake and a little bit of the big block of ice that had formed around Roy."

I looked out the window again. The rain had slowed a bit. I wondered if the problem with Campbell's car was also cracked spark plug wires.

"When you got back here last night, did Campbell's car start right up?" I asked.

"Yup. First crank," said Tom. "That old heap of his overheats all the time. If he ever drove much farther than here or your Uncle Roy's to check up on the place, I'd nag him more about getting a new car. But he almost always stops here when he's on his way there. If I don't see him drive by on his way home, I go out looking for him. He always says he's too old to buy a new car. He may be right."

"I'm thinking of making my way over to Campbell's. I should bring some lunch. Do you have any pastrami?"

"That, a good loaf of pumpernickel, and some beer ought to get you through the afternoon," said Tom.

"Anything but smoked sausage and cheese," I said. "No offense, but it's all I've eaten this week."

Visions of Self-Reliance

I was really pushing it to attempt the drive to Campbell's. It was the farthest point away from Uncle Roy's, and the roads were drenched. As I climbed out of Monson, I started feeling a little better about my decision. If my car stalled, I could roll most of the way back to Randall's Store. I also had beer and the makings for pastrami sandwiches, so if I broke down, I could wait out the worst of the rain before I would need to walk.

Damn, Campbell's road was in rough shape. Where it was steep, which was most of it, the water had formed trenches alongside and, occasionally, washouts all the way across the road. As my car shuddered over the ruts, sometimes moving a foot or two sideways, I thought about turning around. Only there was no place to do it. The trees came right up to the edge.

"Slow and steady," I said aloud. The wind was blowing maple and birch leaves out of the trees in waves. Some of them stuck to my rain-soaked car and windshield. I couldn't wait to top out on the ridge where Campbell's cabin was. I hoped he was there, although if he wasn't at the store, I didn't know where else he might be.

It was some relief when I saw his car parked out front and smoke coming out of his stovepipe. I snagged the grocery bags off the driver's seat and ran through the rain to arrive on his porch.

The door opened, and Campbell frankly looked less excited to see me than I was to see him.

"Thought you'd be hunkered down at Roy's," he said in a way that made me think I shouldn't have come up here at all.

"Me, too," I said. "But to be honest, I found out that I didn't much feel like sitting by the woodstove alone all day. Maybe I'm not as much like Uncle Roy as I thought. I did bring pastrami, pumpernickel, and beer, though."

Campbell stood in the doorway looking at me long enough that I was thankful to be under a roof. "You play cribbage?" he asked.

I nodded yes.

"In that case, come on in."

I always found it interesting that Campbell's cabin was so inviting, even if he didn't seem to be himself. It wasn't like many people went there. For most of the people who lived in these parts, connecting with people was something that required a trip into town. It was one of the benefits of independence—you got to decide when and how much time you spent with other folks. My childhood trips to Uncle Roy's had helped me see what a gift independence could be, spending weeks on end in a cabin without a care about anything except getting the canoe back to shore before dark.

But this week had shown me that while pure self-reliance was a seductive goal, it was nearly impossible to attain. Even those most determined to make it on their own—Uncle Roy, Campbell, and even Jim Whyte, the most mysterious resident of them all—needed people to make their "self-sufficiency" possible. Then there were the degrees of self-sufficiency, which necessarily ebbed as each man aged. Uncle Roy needed help cutting ice. He died sawing logs in anticipation of the winter ahead. Jim Whyte's successive strokes cost him his voice and his independence with cruel speed. I felt sadder for him than for Uncle Roy. At least Uncle Roy died alone in the place he loved. The man from the cabin near Big Wilson Cliffs died in a place where the greatest measure of independence was whether you could walk to the toilet or needed a wheelchair.

I wondered how much Phil Campbell had thought about it. Having seen both men die, he must have at least wondered how his own story would end. But I wasn't going to start the conversation there. Fortunately, he steered me to a safer subject.

"Have a seat. Cut the deck. Low card deals," he said.

"Uncle Roy and I used to play a lot of cribbage. He taught me how to play that summer when I stayed up here. I played it all the way through college, too. Game after game. Sometimes I wonder how I graduated," I said.

"Sounds like you did okay in school just the same," he said. "Tom says you landed a good job down in Portland. Newspaper reporter, right?"

"Not a reporter. Not yet, anyway. Got to work my way up to that," I said.

"Well, you seem to be doing well with it up here," he said.

I sure wasn't expecting that response. Maybe Campbell thought I was prying too much. I felt fortunate that I had cut the low card and pretended to concentrate on my shuffling to buy some time to respond.

"I'm pulling your leg, Ben. You know as well as I do that people up this way only share things if they want to. I wouldn't have told you about Jim Whyte's treasure if I didn't think you could be trusted not to go up there with a shovel. But it did bother me when Tom Randall told me you worked for the newspaper. Because the last thing we need is another bunch of folks rolling into town and digging up that mountainside again."

A big gust of wind slammed against the cabin, rattling the windows behind me. It sounded as if we might blow off the ridge. But Campbell didn't seem too concerned. He must have sat through worse. He wasn't going to let the distraction rob his train of thought, either.

"So, Ben. I need you to promise not to talk about Jim Whyte in the paper."

I picked up my six cards. What a lousy hand. I only had two points in it. Campbell threw two cards in the crib almost immediately. Bad sign, I thought. It usually meant your opponent had a splendid hand even before the game really started.

"Okay. You've got a deal," I said. "I won't write the story for the Portland paper."

"Or any newspaper?" asked Campbell.

I paused for a few seconds. "Or any newspaper," I said.

"Good," said Campbell. He waited a moment, then added, "Best really not to share it with anyone—newspaper or otherwise."

"You have my word," I said.

"Good," he said.

Campbell smoked me. I couldn't remember when I had been dealt such lousy hands. He seemed to score points no matter what I played. He collected the cards, pegs, and game board and pushed them aside.

"What, no rematch?" I asked.

"Not yet," he said.

Campbell stood up from the table and stretched. He was still in good shape for his age. No wonder. There was always work to do at the cabin, either fixing something that paid off right away, like patching the roof, or accomplishing something that paid off later, like cutting and stacking firewood. It was hard for him to sit for too long without getting up to do something. He pulled his flannel shirttails up, plunged his hands into his front pockets, and looked toward the stove.

"Only I know some things that happened at Whyte's," he said. "Not even Tom and Lydia Randall know. Most of the people who could be hurt by it are dead. But some are still with us."

I wondered if he was going to tell the whole story without looking at me. Lots of people did that in this part of Maine. Maybe because they only had a chance to talk with each other while they were doing something else, like haying, fishing, or putting a new roof on a barn.

"For years, I thought I was going to let the story die with me. I never even told Roy. That was the hardest thing of all. I came close, but I kept thinking it was better to wait. I figured I'd tell him when the only people who could still get hurt were out of harm's way. Only problem with that was Roy died before that day ever came. So, I get to tell you instead."

"How many people are still in harm's way?" I asked.

"You'll find out soon enough," he said. Campbell nodded back toward the kitchen counter. "I'm hungry. What about you?"

"Yup," I said. Damn, Campbell was frustrating. He'd come right to the verge of sharing something, then he'd back off. Why did he do that? When I thought of him hiding in the shadows to spy on Jim Whyte, everything began to make sense. Campbell kept a keen eye on the world around him, took everything in, and only shared what he had learned if and when the time and the audience were right. If I was ever going to get the story out of him, I'd need to be patient.

We stood up and walked over toward the kitchen wall. Unlike Uncle Roy's cabin, where the kitchen was a separate room, Campbell's had a large common room across the front. It was a kitchen, dining area, and living room all in one. Only the two bedrooms were partitioned off by the wall behind the woodstove. The bedrooms each had a door that opened out onto the back porch, the one you could see Jim Whyte's ridge from. Because Campbell lived alone, he used one of the bedrooms as a permanent means of accessing the porch. On my first trips here, I had been amazed at how much stuff had piled up on that spare bed—winter jackets and gloves, a few books, shotgun shells, binoculars, and only

Campbell knows what else. One thing for sure, the man had lived alone for a long time. As he sliced the pumpernickel to make our sandwiches, I thought more about Campbell's life of near solitude. With Uncle Roy gone, the only people he ever saw regularly were the Randalls. I wondered if Campbell ever thought about how much he and Jim Whyte had in common or the fact that he outlasted Jim by more than a decade. I also wondered if Campbell ever got scared about how things would turn out for him or whether he only looked down the road as far as he needed to every day, so he wouldn't be scared at all.

After lunch, Campbell insisted on moving to the two most comfortable chairs closer to the woodstove. There was no mistaking the one Campbell used every day. The cushion was about half as thick as the one in the chair he offered me and twice as filthy. Campbell was actually embarrassed about it.

"I'd flip it over, but the other side is worse. Lydia Randall always says she'll get something in Skowhegan for me if I ever need it. I never seem to think about the cushions," he said.

Without leaving his seat, he leaned forward, opened the stove door, and threw another log on the coals.

"Well, I imagine the best place to start this story is at the end of it," said Campbell. "That's the part you know the most about. Then we can go back to the beginning.

"That day I borrowed Tom Randall's camera was the day things went to hell," he said. "Tom loaded the film into the camera in a closet in the back of the store because he said he needed a dark place to do it. It was a nice day, so I decided to wait across the street by my car. When Tom came out with the camera and walked across the street, I could see Fred Hall's son, John, walk behind Tom and into the store. I didn't think to say anything about it because Lydia was already inside. It was when Tom was giving me a few pointers on how to use the camera that I told him why I was using it—to take pictures of the cabin to show to Jim Whyte, so I could find out where he had buried the money. As you know, I almost didn't tell Tom. To this day, I wish I hadn't."

Campbell got up, walked over to the porch door, and opened it just long enough to reach outside for two of the beers. He pulled a church key out of his front pocket, opened his beer, and then handed a beer and the opener to me. The opener said "Schaefer—America's Oldest Lager Beer" on it. I dutifully opened my beer, nodded to Campbell, then handed his beloved opener back to him.

"Well, Tom couldn't keep a secret for more than fifty feet," he said. "The way both of them tell it, Tom stepped foot in the store, saw Lydia, and blurted out, 'Jim Whyte told Campbell there was $40,000 buried by his cabin.' Lydia says she was never more horrified in her life. Tom hadn't seen John Hall. He was hidden by some of the store shelves. But there was no way news like that was going to stay a secret for long. Afterward, I figured the whole town knew before I even got back to my cabin. I was so mad at Tom Randall that I didn't go into his store for a month. Drove to Guilford instead. I wouldn't even pass anywhere near Randall's Store.

"About three weeks into it, Jim Whyte's daughter—who none of us had ever seen or even known about before—showed up from New York with two men who were about her age. They went to Jim's cabin and told everyone else to get out. They stayed for two weeks. After they left, I went up there. What a disaster. Every piece of ground within two hundred yards of that cabin had been turned over with shovels and pickaxes. I was so mad about it that I dropped a big tree in front of Whyte's trail to make it harder for people to get in and out of there. After all, if I hadn't said anything to Randall, the place wouldn't have been dug all to hell."

Campbell shook his head, tugged on his shirtsleeves, and continued to stare toward the woodstove.

"Word is, nobody found anything. If anyone from this town did, you'd know about it. So that leaves his daughter and her friends. They didn't look too pleased when they got on the train out of Onawa. It's been thirteen years, or 'close to fifteen' to Tom Randall's way of thinking. Either way, almost everyone has forgotten about it by now."

Campbell took a swig of beer, then looked over his left shoulder toward the nearest window. The rain had backed off a bit, enough to make him want to bring in a few loads of wood. He handed me one of two canvas slings he used to haul wood in from the woodpile. If I wanted to get my notebook out of my car, this would be the time—before Campbell launched into the best part of the story. But I thought better of it. If I asked to take notes, he might question what I was going to do with the story after all and be less willing to tell all of it. A better choice would be to stop matching Campbell beer for beer and commit as much of the story to memory as I could.

Back inside with enough wood stacked to last Campbell for days, we sat down by the stove again.

"Jim Whyte built his cabin on the ridge and stayed there for thirty-eight years," he said. "I was eighteen when he showed up with his wife Dora and his deed to the land. Back then, if you wanted good-paying work, you had three choices—the slate quarry, the railroad, or the forest. As you know, your Uncle Roy chose the railroad. I went to work for the quarry. In those days, the slate we hauled out of the quarries here went on to become sidewalks, gravestones, billiard tables, roofing tile, and kitchen sinks all over the country. We could barely keep up with the demand until the Great Depression came and nearly shut us down.

"Jim Whyte was twice my age when he hiked up on the ridge with Dora and started building the cabin. 'Course anyone who got past Big Wilson Stream and hiked a short way up the hill could hear the sound of sawing and hammering from first light until long after the sun disappeared. Every once in a while, I'd sneak up to Big Wilson Cliffs to get a look at the progress myself. I'd lie on my stomach and crawl over to the edge so I could look down without them seeing me. Let me tell you, the guy knew what he was doing. Those cabin walls went up fast. He had rigged up some tripods and ropes so he could swing the logs into place and check their fit. If they weren't tight as could be, he'd haul the new log up and out of the way so he could use his draw knife to make it right. Most guys, including your Uncle Roy, made up the difference by putting a fair amount of oakum between the logs. But that hermit made his cabin as tight as a ship's hull. Some would have called it a waste of time to make a building that tight. I would have, too, if that place hadn't gone up about as fast as any cabin I'd ever seen.

"One time, I almost got caught spying on them. It was July that year they were building the cabin. It was hot as hell in the quarry that day. When I got out of work, the first thing I wanted to do was jump into Big Wilson Stream to wash off the dust and sweat. After my swim, I climbed up to Big Wilson Cliffs. It had been a few weeks since I'd taken a look at Whyte's cabin, and I knew if there was any breeze within a few miles, it would be up there. I had just gotten to the top and was still catching my breath—it was that soon after I got there—when I heard some voices coming up out of the woods below me. I dove into the spruce stand behind me. It was a good thing I was skinny back then; those trees were packed in so tight. I squeezed between two of them and ducked down right when Jim and Dora climbed up onto the ridge. Thirty seconds earlier and they would have seen me.

"They stood taking in the view for a while. Then they sat down next to each other on the rocks, looking out over everything. I could tell it wasn't their first time up there. They didn't spend any time talking about what they could see like you do when you get on top of a mountain for the first time.

"After a bit, they turned so their backs were facing me and they were looking down at their cabin. Even though I was only twenty yards away, I couldn't hear their conversation because they were back-to. But there was a fair amount of talking on his part and almost none on her part. The way they were sitting and talking made me think that their partnership was more like a business than a marriage—as it turned out, I would be right about that. After fifteen minutes or so, they stood up and began climbing down toward their cabin again. It wasn't more than ten minutes after that when I could hear Jim Whyte's saw cutting through a log down below. I pushed my way out through the spruce and crawled to the edge of the cliff to take a look. I'll be damned if they weren't almost done building that place. The walls were done, and he was sawing through one of the last roof rafters. That's all I needed to know. I was glad I hadn't been caught up there, but I paid the price for staying hidden. I was covered in blackfly bites and spruce needles. On the way out, I stopped for another swim.

"After that day, I only snuck up onto Big Wilson Cliffs one more time. By late September, I figured they'd be all moved in and getting ready for winter, so I climbed up to take a look. I was right. The cabin was all done. I could see the both of them down in the yard—at least they weren't climbing up the trail toward me! The cabin had something I hadn't seen before—big wooden panels or shutters, I guess you'd call 'em. I took out my binoculars to get a closer look. The shutters were hinged at the top and could be lowered by ropes that went through holes next to the windows."

"They were hiding from someone," I said.

Campbell turned toward me for the first time since he started talking. "Yes, they were. And I decided that I needed to get off that cliff before they saw me. Once I got down into the woods, I ran down as fast as I could. I didn't get near that cabin again for a couple of years. By that time, Dora was gone, and Tessa had moved in. As you know by now, the only time people ever saw Tessa was when she went to New York with her husband. I don't know how she did it. Even I need to go into town to talk to folks now and again. And if Jim was hiding from someone, why was he the one who came into town, not her?

"Anyhow, one day when I was in Randall's Store, Tom mentioned that the Whytes had left for New York for a few days. That was all I needed to hear. I found Roy and convinced him we should go to see the cabin while they were gone. Before we crossed the bridge they made over Big Wilson Stream, I mentioned the shutters over the windows to Roy. Well, that was enough to make him think we were stupid to take the trail up there. He was convinced it was booby-trapped. So instead, we hiked up to Big Wilson Cliffs. We dropped down over the cliff, the way Jim and Dora Whyte had that time I saw them. Neither one of us thought it would be a good idea to just walk across the clearing toward the cabin—it was too out in the open. If Tom Randall was wrong and the Whytes hadn't left, we'd be caught. So, we worked our way around the edge of the woods to the back and hiked toward the back of the cabin on the outhouse trail. By then, we knew the cabin was empty and they really were away.

"I was right about his carpentry. The place was really well put together. Those end notches on the logs were so tight that he didn't even need to stuff them with mud or moss. We doubted he'd even need to after the logs had baked in the sun for a few years. We'd never seen that before. Just look over there at the corner of my cabin. For years I've had to stuff those gaps before winter came. Roy and I walked along the left side of the cabin and out to the front. Neither one of us dared to get on the porch in case it was booby-trapped, but we did take a good look at those shutters. They were down, of course. Each one had two holes in it, one above the other."

"One for looking at who was coming and one for shooting at them," I said.

"Right. That was all the convincing we needed to get away from that place and make tracks for Big Wilson Cliffs again. Neither one of us said anything about that day for quite a few years, except to each other every once in a while when we were out fishing or something. We were afraid that somehow Jim Whyte would get wind of the fact we'd been poking around up there.

"But I'll tell you, the next big thing to happen at Whyte's cabin was something that got the whole town buzzing! Just after World War I broke out, a couple of FBI guys showed up at Randall's Store asking where Jim Whyte lived. They also asked if there was more than one way to get to and from the cabin. Of course, Tom told them about the hiking trail up from Big Wilson Stream and the road Whyte had cut for his car on the back of the ridge.

"The rumor was that the feds asked Jim Whyte about his time in the German Navy and whether he was sympathetic to the German cause in the war. You can bet that took everyone in town by surprise. Imagine what Jim Whyte thought when the feds showed up! I'll tell you one thing—he must have done a good job of telling them what they needed to hear because they didn't come back."

"The German Navy? You're kidding," I said.

"Not kidding at all. He joined when he was a teenager in the 1870s. He'd gotten in a big fight with his father and left home."

"Did he say what the fight was about?"

"Yes, but only after I'd gotten to know him for quite a while. I was probably the only one he ever told, at least up this way. More people knew about it down in New York. It was kind of a big deal down there. When Whyte was fifteen, he took a girlfriend for a walk in Central Park. He never explicitly said as much, but I got the impression that this girl was his first real love. Whyte said they had a wonderful stroll through the park, laughing and talking about anything that came to mind. After they had walked for quite a ways, they stopped to sit on a park bench. Whyte put his arm around her, and she sat with her head leaning against his shoulder and neck. After a while, his arm was getting numb, so he needed move it. To his shock, when he did, she slumped forward and fell to the ground. She had died right there in his arms."

"How horrible," I said.

"Yes. Afterward there was an inquest and an investigation that went on for some months. It was quite a sensation in the city newspapers. Whyte was cleared, of course, but his father was upset about the harm that had been done to the family name. One night, they got into a big quarrel about it. That's when Jim walked out the door and set his sights on joining the German Navy. He was sixteen when he signed on."

"What a story! When did he tell you all this?" I asked.

"A few years after Tessa left. Jim started coming down into town a lot more after that. It took more than twenty years for us to find out that he was cut out to be sociable and Tessa wasn't. I think he was fine as long as he had someone there to spin his yarns to. But my guess is that after two decades of listening to his stories, she'd had enough."

"What happened to her?"

"Nobody knew for the longest time. There were rumors that she went back home to Milo, but because nobody around here really knew her, there was no reason to find out.

"It wasn't until several years after Tessa left that Jim Whyte and I became friends," Campbell said. "I was at Randall's Store when he came in to buy supplies. I was standing at the counter talking to Tom when Whyte walked in. You know as well as I do that you can look through the front window to see if any customers are at the counter before you go in. I always figured if the hermit wanted the store to himself, he could have waited for me to leave. But this time, he decided to walk right in. Given the stories about how much of a loner he was and what I'd seen myself up until then, I was surprised.

"Tom immediately introduced us to each other. Said it was finally time for the two 'ridgetoppers' of the area to meet or something like that. 'Course he meant that we were the only two men crazy enough to live on top of mountains. Whyte was intrigued by that. 'Where do you live?' he asked. I had sort of heard his voice before, when he was facing away from me on Big Wilson Cliffs, but this time, I heard him clear as a bell."

"When was that?" I asked.

"1924, I think. Anyways, I told Whyte where I lived, but he didn't show much interest in visiting me. I mean, he didn't ask how to get to my cabin or anything. But he did ask me if I knew where he lived. 'Right next to Big Wilson Cliffs,' I said before I could think about it. Whyte pushed his hat back off of his forehead a bit and said, 'Quite the view from up there, isn't it?' Well, I wasn't going to deny I'd been up there, so I said something about going up there to watch sunsets when I was much younger. 'Years ago, I could have sworn I saw someone up there watching me build my cabin,' said Whyte. 'It was just every now and again. Figured he had his curiosity filled and that was that. Never got too concerned about it.'

"I decided not to say anything about it being me, at least not for a while. Tom saw a way to get me out of the conversation by handing me my sack of groceries. As I turned to leave, Jim Whyte had the last word. 'If you'd like to see my cabin, come on up. There's a bridge over Big Wilson Stream and a hiking trail up to my clearing,' he said. I told him I just might take him up on that."

Campbell got up from his chair, rolled a squat log from near the woodpile in front of his chair, and flipped it flat side up. He got back in his chair and set his feet on the log.

"I get a new one every year," said Campbell. "In the spring, I'll burn up this one. Makes the room cleaner."

He seemed to want affirmation for his ingenuity, so I smiled and nodded.

"Well, I didn't wait long. It was the Saturday after I met him at Randall's Store. It was a nice fall afternoon—like the one we had on the lake a couple of days ago. I drove down into the valley and parked near Big Wilson Stream. As I crossed Whyte's bridge, I thought about the time I was last there with your Uncle Roy and how we had been worried that the trail was booby trapped. Just before I got to his clearing, there were signs posted in the trees: 'Beware of Target Shooting,' they said. Well, hell, I stopped and yelled up toward the cabin. Whyte yelled right back from the porch to come on up. Turns out he was drinking coffee out there and saw me all along. When I got to the cabin, he shook my hand and asked me to join him for a cup."

Campbell turned toward me. "It was the first time I'd been in the cabin, of course," he said. "I'd gotten a couple of good looks at it from the outside, but I wasn't prepared for what he had done inside. It was furnished not just comfortably, but richly. It was immaculate and well designed. He had blocked the kitchen off from the main part of the cabin with a wall. He put a door in it like I'd never seen before. Somehow, he figured out how to make the door open into whichever room he was entering. 'I wanted to be able to carry stuff to and from the kitchen and kick the door open with my foot,' he said. Then there were the guns. Every wall had at least one loaded gun hanging on it. There were rifles, shotguns, pistols, you name it. All different styles and gauges. There was a pair of binoculars hanging on a nail near the door. It was true, he was worried about someone finding him there. Someone other than the FBI—he had gotten them to go away using nothing but words."

Campbell stood up and walked over to the wall behind the wood-stove. He held his hand as high as he could reach.

"What's that, about eight feet?" he asked.

"I'd say so," I said.

"Whyte's bookshelves had to be higher than that, twelve feet, maybe. He had hundreds of books in there. Books about shipping, hunting, history, canning, you name it. Some were written in German, Italian, and French. And I forgot to mention the kitchen. He had the best sets of plates, bowls, and sterling silver I'd ever seen. Must have gotten them in Europe or something. That wasn't all. He had good rugs on the floors, a trunk full of linens, and some really fine fly rods. You can imagine how much I wanted to try one of those out, but I didn't know him well enough to ask.

"As I said, it was a nice day, so we went outside and sat on the porch. I didn't stay long that first time I went to see him. It was fall, and everyone, including me, had lots of chores to take care of before winter. But a few things from that visit really stuck with me. One was what he said about Tessa. He was going into another winter without her there and it was on his mind, I guess. 'On days like this, she would be busy inside canning applesauce,' he said. 'It was a full day's work, but when she was done, we'd have a full shelf in the cellar to help tide us over. But she's gone now. She'd had enough of living up here, and I didn't want to leave.'

"As he talked about it, he got a little choked up. He cleared his throat, shook his head a little as if to snap himself out of it, and changed the subject. He said he thought it was the right time of day to show me something. As he was leading me back into the cabin, I was struck by how neat the place was. Everything was shipshape. His floor was so clean he must have swept it every day. There weren't any dirty dishes in the kitchen, either. He must have washed them and put them away after every meal. He walked over to a peephole he had cut in the back wall of the cabin and looked through it. Then he turned toward me with a big smile and held a finger in front of his mouth. He went to the corner of the kitchen and grabbed a ten-foot fly rod. He motioned for me to look through the peephole. When I looked through, I saw a deer standing about five feet from the other side of the wall. I'd never seen a deer that close unless I'd shot it during hunting season. This one kept twitching its ear like it had a mosquito flying around it or something. Then I noticed that there was something actually poking her. Jim Whyte had stuck his fly rod out through another hole in the wall and was tickling the deer's ear. She started scratching at it with her rear leg, just like a dog would. I pulled away from the peephole and looked over at Whyte. He was laughing so hard he was practically doubled over on the floor. I think he must have been planning out that gag for quite a while. It sure was funny."

"Seems like he wasn't exactly a loner," I said. "He certainly opened up to you."

"I think he was only a loner out of necessity. He wasn't shy about telling stories, that's for sure. But that first visit didn't last much longer. He said he had a lot of work to do around the cabin and that maybe we could chat again sometime. As I walked back down his trail, I didn't have any idea how soon I'd be back."

"What did he look like in those days?" I asked.

"He was lean and medium height, and his hair was almost all gray by then. I'd say he was around sixty years old about that time. He almost always wore a plaid flannel shirt and some kind of hat. I never saw him without a hat. He shaved every day. And he smiled when he talked. Once

I got to know him, I was most surprised by how talkative and happy he was. I'll tell you another funny story about him. I wouldn't believe it if I didn't see it myself."

"I'm all ears," I said.

"I hiked up to Whyte's one morning. As was my habit by then, I yelled up to the cabin when I got to the target practice signs. He came out onto the porch and waved me up. 'Just in time, I'm making flapjacks,' he said. Sure enough, as soon as I walked in, I could smell them. He had two already made and another one on the griddle. When he was ready to flip it over, he said, 'Watch this!'"

Campbell ran to his kitchen, took a cast-iron skillet off the wall, and hustled back into the room.

"You've got to imagine this. Whyte's cabin had a skylight in the kitchen. In the summer months, he took the glass off to keep the cabin cooler. Suddenly, Whyte took the skillet and flung that pancake up and out of the cabin through the skylight. He ran out the back door, held the skillet in front of him, and caught the pancake before it hit the ground. He came back into the kitchen with a big smile on his face. 'I had to practice that for quite a while,' he said. Yup, Jim Whyte had a lot of fun at that cabin. He wasn't one of those grumpy hermits like me."

"Oh, you're not that bad," I said.

"Really?" said Campbell. "I'll have to work on that. Don't want to ruin my image."

Campbell took his legs off his ottoman log and stood up. He walked toward the spare bedroom, disappeared for a few moments, and then came back with something in his right hand.

"Here," he said. "I took these photos with Tom Randall's camera. After Whyte died, I went up to the cabin. I figured I'd bought the film, I might as well use it how I intended. You can have them. I won't be needing them."

There were half a dozen black-and-white snapshots in all. As I was wondering why there weren't more, Campbell answered me.

"I only took about half a roll's worth of photos up there. Those were the only good ones that came out of it. I ended up taking some pictures of Randall's Store to use up the roll and gave them to Tom along with the negatives," he said.

For the first time since I arrived at Campbell's, it seemed like we were having a real conversation as opposed to me wondering if he would feel inconvenienced if I said something. I didn't want to lose the momentum. There were some photos from the inside of the ransacked cabin, so I started there.

"How did you get inside? Was the door unlocked?" I asked.

"Unlocked? Hell, no!" he said. "The bastards pried the hasp off. They probably took an axe up there with them. Either that, or they stole a piece of pipe from under the porch or something," said Campbell. "Like I said, it was less than a day after I put Whyte on the train for New Jersey that they went in there and took everything. I went up there two days later to check on the cabin and it was stripped bare."

"And nobody knows who did it?" I asked.

"I wouldn't say that. Some of us had a good idea, but it wasn't anything that could ever be proven. I'm sure a lot of the stuff ended up with the thieves' relatives in Portland or Boston or something."

I looked closely at the second photo. I could see the nails in the front wall where Whyte had hung his pistols and rifles.

I handed the photo to Campbell. "I take it that tenpenny nail next to the door must be where he hung his binoculars," I said.

"That's it, alright," Campbell said as he squinted a little. "You can just make out where the binoculars made a mark from swinging back and forth when he hung them back up."

"Did you ever find out who he was hiding from?"

"Eventually," said Campbell. "When I first went up there to see him, I needed to get an idea so I wouldn't be afraid of getting shot if I went back up there. What I came to realize in those first years after Tessa left was that Jim wasn't afraid of anyone from around here anymore. That he'd finally reached the point where he felt he could trust at least a few of us—me, Tom and Lydia Randall, and a few others, to be sure."

I noticed he didn't mention Uncle Roy. I wanted to get to that part, but Campbell was on a roll, and I knew better than to interrupt.

"Whatever he was afraid of was always on his mind," said Campbell. "That first visit when I walked into his cabin with him to get that first mug of coffee, I noticed the stack of old issues of the Police Gazette next to the woodstove."

"Police Gazette!" I barely said the words before I started laughing. Everyone in the newspaper business (and for that matter, most people who weren't) knew about the scandalous Police Gazette, whose pages were filled with girlie pictures, ads for pimple cream, and boxing coverage. It seemed an odd choice, even for a hermit, especially since it would have to be mailed from New York.

"Why in the world would he have a subscription to that?" I asked. "And how did he get it? I can't see Tom Randall keeping it a secret."

"Me either," said Campbell. "That's one reason he didn't have them mailed to Monson. He had them mailed to the Guilford post office instead. He went down there twice a week to get them. He read them to see what the police in New York were up to. But that wasn't the oddest thing about his trips down there. Nope. The oddest thing was that they didn't know him as Jim Whyte."

"How's that?" I asked.

"Because his post office box was registered to the son of a German carriage-maker from New York City, a man named William Boscene."

"Was Boscene someone he'd met?" I asked, thinking that using an alias would help Jim Whyte hide more effectively if people came to Guilford looking for him.

Campbell looked at me. He almost let out a laugh of his own. He lifted his hat with his right hand, pulled his wrist across his forehead, and set his hat back down a little higher than it had been.

"You could say that," he said, pausing for effect. "Because Jim Whyte and William Boscene were the same man."

Many Stories Become One

"It took me a while to put everything together," said Campbell. "He loved to tell stories, but each one was like a one-act play pulled from his past without any reference point. Sometimes they took place in Europe somewhere, sometimes in Idaho, and sometimes a lot farther away than that. It was all confusing at first trying to figure out what happened when. I wondered if all of his tales were true. At first, I thought he might have been adding himself into stories he had heard in his travels. He had enough time alone to invent stories, after all. But I came around to the idea that he really could have led the life he described after all."

"But what about William…*Bossen*, was it?" I asked.

"Bo-scene," said Campbell. "*B-o-s-c-e-n-e*. He only spelled it out for me once and asked me to never call him by that name. He was likely ashamed of it because of his father."

Campbell sat back in his chair and put his feet back on the ottoman log. I hated to break his line of thought, but I couldn't risk my one shot at getting the story straight.

"Do you mind if I write some things down?" I asked. "I have a notepad in the car."

Campbell took a long time to say something. He stared straight ahead with his feet up on that log. I couldn't even see him breathing. It seemed the only thing moving around were his thoughts.

"I'll just write a few words here and there. Like *Boscene*—not whole sentences or anything," I said.

At last, Campbell lifted his right foot and placed it on the edge of the log so his knee was bent. He took a deep breath.

"Only if you promise that none of it comes out until after I'm dead," he said. "The first part I don't care much about. But like I said, the last part has to stay in this room. I'll tell you when you have to put the pen down."

"Thank you, Phil," I said. I got up to get my notebook. It sounded funny to call him by his first name, but I still felt Campbell was a better friend of Uncle Roy than of me. Perhaps it needed to stay that way. When I sat down by the fire again, I thought I'd made a mistake. Campbell had both feet on the edge of the ottoman log, and he was pushed way back in his chair.

I set my notebook and pen next to me on the floor. "I can skip taking notes," I said.

He nodded his head upward a few times to indicate I should pick my stuff up off the floor and start writing.

"He was born in New York City in the late 1850s," he said. "Like I told you, his father was a carriage-maker. They never got along. Jim—or should I say, William—couldn't stand him. He never talked about it except to say that right after his sixteenth birthday, they got into that big fight and he left home. He wanted to get as far away from that man as he could, so he joined the German Navy."

"That must have done the trick," I said.

"And then some. He didn't come back to the states for another fifteen years."

"He was in the German Navy for fifteen years?" I asked.

"I didn't say that," he said. "Just that he was gone. I never could tell how many years he was a naval officer. Likely a handful or so. But he stayed at sea. He became an officer in the German merchant marine. He showed me his officer's uniform one time—brought it out from his bedroom, neatly pressed and still looking like new. He told me he'd worked on whaling ships and steamers that went all over the world—the Barbary Coast, Port Bald, the South Seas, and China. There were lots of trips to China. He kept a few trinkets from his years at sea. A telescope from the German Navy, a pocket compass, and a few other things."

"He gave the telescope to Tom Randall," I said.

"That he did. It's a nice one," said Campbell. "He kept more things from his travels after he left the service. He must have made good money then. He bought emerald rings, a gold pocket watch, nice clothes, a lot of things that struck his fancy."

"On a deckhand's pay?" I asked.

"Oh no. The way he put it, every captain, whether hunting for whales or hauling barrels of molasses, wanted him on the crew. He worked his way up to second in command for a while, then made enough money to buy his own boat. He made lots of money in those days. He was on top of the world. At some point, he sold his boat and became a pearl diver. It seemed every decision he made brought him more adventures and more money. By the time he got done, he had learned six languages and made friends in practically every civilized country in the world—and in a number of uncivilized ones, too."

"Got done? When was that?" I asked without looking up from writing *pearl diver* in my notebook.

"1892. He was thirty-four years old and had been away from home more than half his life. He said that a lot. He'd seen much of the world and had enjoyed almost all of what he'd done, but he got the feeling it was time to stay in one place for a while."

That's an understatement, I thought. The guy stayed in Onawa for almost forty years. I decided not to say anything and let Campbell keep talking.

"First thing he did when he landed in New York was go back to his neighborhood. He didn't know what to expect from his father, so he spent some time casing the place. It didn't take him long to find out that his father had died some years before. The way he told it, his mother almost fainted when he showed up at the door. It took weeks for him to tell her about his adventures, and I'm certain he didn't share all of them. He ended up staying with her for a while. Sometime in the first few weeks home, he met a neighborhood girl. They married a few months later, and he started a new life as a husband and father."

"A father? I guess he was committed to settling down," I said.

"Actually, he wasn't. At least with her. And that's where the life of William Boscene turned into the adventures of Jim Whyte. He never told me why he left her and the baby behind. In fact, he never even told me either of their names. What I do know is that he showed up in Onawa not long after he left New York. That was 1893."

"The first time Tom and Lydia Randall met him," I said.

"Yes."

"But he didn't show up again for two years."

"That's because he went to Idaho to prospect for gold. He told me he needed to get away from the east coast for a while."

"That's the second time that happened," I said.

"And the last," said Campbell. "He said he needed to go someplace and think and that he might as well try to make some money while he was at it. Idaho had just become a state back then. They called it Idaho Territory before that. There was a lot of talk about the rivers flowing with gold in those days, so Jim decided to try his hand at it. He was only gone for those two years. He said he didn't do well as a prospector, although you could never be certain with him when it came to money."

"And when he showed up in Onawa again, he was Jim Whyte with a wife named Dora and a thirty-acre deed to the property above Big Wilson Stream?" I asked.

"Yes, but as far as renaming himself, he did that right when he left New York a few years before."

"I can understand why," I said. "I imagine there were a few people upset with him back there. No wonder he lived with one eye looking out the window and loaded guns nearby."

"That's not the only reason, but it's a good enough one," said Campbell.

"Do you think he bought his land with Idaho gold?" I asked.

"Like I said, it's hard to say. It wasn't any of my business, but I think he could have afforded it whether he went to Idaho or not. But when he got here, all of his and Dora's energy went into building that cabin and getting moved in before the first snowfall."

Campbell's back porch, the one I entered through, faced west. During our discussion, the sun had broken through the overcast a few times. Now it did again, creating long patterns of light across the floor and shadows of our heads against the back wall.

"Looks like a good time to go outside for a bit," Campbell said. "I'll be spending most of the winter in here by the fire, so it's good to get outside while we can."

I put on my coat and stepped onto the covered porch. The rain had taken down a lot of leaves. Those that remained were gorgeously illuminated by the late afternoon sun. The maples' trunks, stained black by the rain, created a stunning backdrop for the golden hues.

I leaned against the front railing and gazed up at the sky. The sun wouldn't be shining on us for long. A thick band of nasty, dark clouds was gathering over the ridge. I wished I had more time to think before Campbell came outside, but it would have to wait.

Over the last few minutes he must have been thinking about how Jim Whyte bought his land, because the first thing Campbell talked about when he stepped through the door was how he acquired his own piece of the world.

"My father built this cabin," he said. "Every time I walk out onto one of my porches, I think about how smart he was to put it where he did. I get the morning sun on the other porch and the sunset from this one. Not only that, but being up here on the ridge means there's almost always a breeze on hot summer nights."

I heard what Campbell said, but I only nodded. My thoughts were still absorbed by the hermit who changed his name and apparently left his family in the lurch.

"Do you think Dora was the woman he married in New York? If she was, wouldn't their daughter have been with them?" I asked.

"No. I'm convinced that Dora wasn't his wife. I think she was someone Whyte met in his travels. He just introduced her as his wife. Whatever they had between them didn't last long. I always had the feeling that she felt obliged to stay until the cabin was finished. But it only took one Maine winter to convince her that she needed to carve out a life somewhere far from Onawa."

"And no one ever saw her again?" I asked.

"Nope. My guess is she went back to New York, or wherever she came from."

Both of us stood there looking out at the trees and the line of clouds. As the silence settled over us, I wondered if Campbell wanted to take a break from telling me about Jim Whyte for the day. I started regretting my decision to get my notebook out of the car. Even though he told me it was all right to jot some things down, I felt that some of the spontaneity left the room as soon as I picked up my pencil. When and if we resumed our chat, I decided I'd better leave my notebook hidden away.

Campbell leaned against a porch post and surveyed his clearing. A fair number of maple branches had come down in the wind.

"Well, I've got a little work to do. I need to bust up those branches for kindling and pile it up in the shed," he said.

I didn't need to ask. I knew he meant right now, not some nameless day in the future.

"You want some help?"

"No. I'll take care of it just fine," he said.

His words stung as if I were suddenly the boy who'd been rejected by his dad. Wow. I hadn't been prepared for that. Campbell didn't seem to notice and kept talking.

"I'm used to doing it on my own. I know where it needs to be stacked and such," he said. "I have some other things I need to do, too. What do you say we meet here tomorrow afternoon around two o'clock?"

Apparently this was going to be the way it was with Campbell. He'd let pieces of the story out, then redraw the boundary. Well, at least he's willing to keep chatting, I thought. I turned to him and said, "Only if I get a chance for a cribbage rematch before we talk."

On my way back to Uncle Roy's, I decided that taking a break in the story was for the best. This way, I'd get to go back to the camp and fill in details in my notebook while the story was still manageable. If I had stayed, I wasn't sure I'd get the unedited version out of Campbell's mouth, anyway. Going back there with a fresh set of questions and my notebook stashed out of sight would give me a better chance of learning the truth. Besides, I had an errand to run in the morning that I wanted to get to before we talked again.

A Side Trip into the Past

Milo, Maine, was about a forty-mile drive from Uncle Roy's. I didn't know what I expected to find there, but if nothing else, I wanted to get a feel for Tessa Whyte's hometown. I told myself that the only thing that would keep me from going there was pouring rain, but I knew it was a lie. The only thing that would keep me from going would be trees crashing down to block the roads.

I had heard of Milo, but I'd never seen it. I knew it was a railroad town like Onawa, but one of the reasons I'd never been there is that it was served by a different line. The Canadian Pacific went through Onawa, running toward Vancouver, British Columbia, in the west and St. John, New Brunswick, in the east. Milo was a stop on the Bangor and Aroostook Railroad, which ran north-south and carried lumber to mills all over Maine and passengers to Bangor, then Portland, where they could catch trains to Boston and beyond.

The sky was just beginning to lighten when I walked through the clearing toward my car. It wasn't raining anymore, and the lowest level of clouds was streaming over the top of Borestone Mountain from west to east. It was a good omen. With any luck, I'd be driving to Campbell's later in the day under bright sunshine.

There weren't many people on the road to Milo. This was a still remote part of Maine. Cabins and homes were clustered around towns with long stretches of spruce, hemlock, hills, and lakes in between.

About a third of the way there, I drove past the road sign pointing to Guilford, the place where Jim Whyte once had a post office box under the name William Boscene. I briefly thought about taking a detour to go there, but it was too early to visit the post office, and I doubted they would share anything with me even if they were open. As it was, I thought I was pushing it to explore Milo and get back to Campbell's by two o'clock.

When I rolled into town, I was surprised to find it was so much larger than Monson. I figured it would have about the same number of people. But the main street had all sorts of shops, a general store, two clothing stores, two barbershops, and a few restaurants. There wasn't much going on in town—most of the shops hadn't opened for the day—so I decided to start trying to find out about Tessa Whyte by looking at the family gravestones.

The only cemetery in town, Evergreen Cemetery, was expansive, flat, and devoid of trees. It was a bit disconcerting. I hadn't been to a lot of cemeteries, but those I knew usually had their share of shrubs and pine trees. What it meant was that I was sure to be seen there, so I'd have to be quick if I didn't want to raise suspicion.

I drove past all of the graves to see if I could spot the Mooers family plot. Just as I turned onto the third dirt road dissecting the cemetery from front to back, I found it—a large brown stone on a granite base with the name "Mooers" engraved across the top. I rummaged through my rucksack for my notebook and pencil, got out of my car, and walked over for a closer look. The names on the stone showed promise. The birth and death dates of the mother and father seemed to fit the right time frame, anyway. I started writing.

Charles N. Mooers, Dec 21, 1835–July 15, 1920

Ann M. Monroe, wife, Mar. 13, 1840–Nov. 24, 1912

Mary Ann, dau., June 27, 1865–Jan. 18, 1867

John Albert, son, Nov. 14, 1875–Feb 1, 1942

Next to the Mooers gravestone was a headstone placed in the ground. When I read the inscription, I gasped. It said "Lizzie Whyte." There was nothing engraved on the slab except her name. I had no idea who Lizzie Whyte was, but I figured since she was buried here alongside the Mooers that she was probably related to Tessa and Jim. It was another question I'd have to ask Campbell.

As I was about to walk away from the graves, I heard the sound of car tires on gravel. Either someone had called the sheriff, or he saw me when he was driving by. Either way, I had company. He waved me over to his open window.

"Can I help you with something?" he asked.

"No, sir. I was looking for a distant relative's grave and I found it," I said. "I was just getting ready to leave when you drove up."

"Who's your relative?" he asked.

"The Mooers," I said. As soon as I blurted it out, I hoped I hadn't made a mistake. Almost everyone in Maine had some kind of connection. With my luck, the sheriff really was related to the Mooers.

"I noticed the Maine plates on your car. Where are you from?" he asked.

"Portland. My mother is related to the Mooers somehow. Second cousin removed or something like that," I said. "I never get those things right." I felt the back of my neck getting warmer while I wondered if my lies would pass muster.

The sheriff chuckled. "I know what you mean. Well, I'm afraid you aren't going to find any Mooers in Milo other than the ones on that gravestone," he said. "The only one left from that family moved down to Bangor to live with her sister-in-law Alice after her brother John died a few years ago. If you want to see her, that's where she'll be."

"Thank you. I appreciate it," I said before turning to walk back to my car. Thankfully, the sheriff drove off first. I jotted down a quick note about Tessa and Alice Mooers living in Bangor, then retraced my route back to Monson. There was nothing left to learn about Tessa or Milo, at least for now, and this way I'd have plenty of time to stop at Randall's Store for lunch before heading to Campbell's.

On my way back to Monson, the storm finally blew out of the area. It felt so good to see the sun again. The soil was so saturated that ground fog filled the low spots to the sides of the road. It was always beautiful in this part of the state, but the rafts of low clouds made the woods feel mystical. It reminded me of one of Uncle Roy's old sayings, and I said it aloud as I drove. "The fog was so thick, even the birds were walking." I smiled until I remembered what I was doing, driving and hiking around trying to dig up the story of someone he didn't like. After all, I wouldn't be doing it if he were still alive. But then I thought about something else Uncle Roy taught me. It had to do with what he'd said about things being uncomfortable when you were climbing a mountain, but you forgot about that once you gained the view. Could it be that my worries about upsetting Uncle Roy or asking too many questions about Jim Whyte were the things I had to work through on my way to something else?

Both Tom and Lydia were at the store when I got back to town. Tom had seen me pull up and had already poured a cup of coffee for me by the time I walked in.

"You on your way back to Campbell's?" he asked.

"Not until I eat some lunch," I said. "I'm starving. I already took a trip over to Milo today."

"Milo," said Tom. "I thought we told you to leave poor Tessa alone."

"I didn't even mention her name," I said. "I just wanted to get a feel for where she grew up. All I did was drive through the town, visit the graveyard, and come right back."

"I wish you'd just asked me," said Tom. "I could have told you that the town she grew up in isn't anything like the town that's there now. Forty years ago, the Bangor and Aroostook Railroad bought Milo Junction, a half-mile outside of Milo. They sunk a million dollars into that town. Built a new train station, a forty-room boarding house, a bunch of houses, and even a casino. It tripled the size of the town, practically overnight."

"They used that yard to work on their railroad cars," said Lydia, who was seated at big table in the front window and motioned me over to take a seat. "My friend Anna Byrd from Milo says the noise from that place kept them up at all hours. Between that and fifty or so trains coming through every day, Milo really changed. It's slowed down a little in the past few years, though. Not quite as many trains, but still quite a few."

Tom glanced out the window and seeing no customers, walked over and sat in the chair closest to the register. "So, what did you find in the graveyard?" he asked.

"The Mooers family plot and a few big surprises. The sheriff pulled in not long after I got there. He told me that Tessa's brother John died five years ago, and she moved to Bangor to live with her sister-in-law afterward. The second surprise was a headstone next to the Mooers gravestone that said Lizzie Whyte."

Lydia gasped. "Oh my gosh. I can't believe it. He had his mother buried in Milo. All we knew was that she wasn't buried here in Monson."

"His mother? I assumed it was his daughter," I said.

"Well, I'll be," said Tom. "There's an irony for ya. He had his mother, who he always visited in New York, buried up here, then the old coot died in New Jersey and was buried down there."

"For many years, while Tessa was still with him, they'd go down to visit her," said Lydia. "He said she was in a home for the infirm and he wanted to make sure they were taking good care of her. But around 1915, they had her moved to Monson to live at Swanson's nursing home."

"She'd lost her mind by then. Barely made sense at all," said Tom. "She died here in town, but the body was shipped somewhere for burial. We always figured it was New York. We never would have guessed it was Milo. That's about all we know about Whyte's mother. Maybe Campbell knows more."

"I don't know how much more Campbell wants to tell me," I said. "He seemed a little, well, *uncomfortable* isn't quite the right word, but something changed when we were talking yesterday."

"Well, he's been keeping something to himself all these years. Maybe now that he's close to letting it out, he's having second thoughts. Pretty understandable, if you ask me," said Tom.

"Well, if he doesn't share it today, he may never," I said. "I've got to get back to Portland tomorrow, and I don't know when I'll get up here again."

Campbell's Secret

I drove to Campbell's camp road and sat at the bottom of the hill for a while. I was still running early and needed a few minutes to prepare. While yesterday's meeting had been interesting, even congenial at times, it made me feel uncomfortable. It wasn't just that Campbell had shut down the Jim Whyte conversation for the day, it was the way he did it. Earlier in the day, we had taken breaks, then picked up where we left off. It was a normal rhythm, like taking a break from paddling the canoe, then starting up again when your partner dips the paddle into the water. But something had made Campbell clam up. I knew that the pile of branches in the yard was only an excuse for calling it a day. I suspected Tom Randall was right. We had covered a lot of ground and were getting so close to Campbell's part of the story that he was rethinking how much to share with me. I was certain that my trip to get the notebook hadn't helped.

I got out of my car and leaned against the hood. The day had heated up enough for me to unzip my jacket partway. There was hardly any breeze, and the sun felt glorious. It was a good place to stand and think.

Surprisingly, my first thought was to leave. If Campbell was having second thoughts about saying anything more to me, what was I doing here? I could just go back to Uncle Roy's and get in one last afternoon of fishing, then drive back to Portland in the morning. I tried convincing myself that I'd had a good week of being outdoors and getting to know Tom and Lydia Randall and Uncle Roy's friend Campbell a little better, and that was good enough.

But it wasn't good enough. Just like it hadn't been good enough for Campbell to see Jim Whyte signaling the train from Big Wilson Cliffs without finding out more. Or it hadn't been good enough for Tom and Lydia Randall to keep Jim Whyte's adventures a secret, at least from me.

So, at this very place on the outskirts of Monson, I made a decision that would change everything. I was going to drive up that hill to Campbell's. But when I got there, it would be on Phil Campbell's terms. I'd keep my notebook in the car, and I'd listen to what he had to say. My only job would be to take it all in. If that meant staying for twenty minutes, two hours, or until the sun went down, it didn't matter. I'd just let the whole thing unfold in front of me.

My poor car labored all the way up the road. I spent most of my time in first gear steering around puddles and trying to keep all four tires on dirt. When I topped out, then dropped into Campbell's clearing, he was on a ladder sawing a low branch out of a maple. He didn't turn around, but he gave a small wave of acknowledgment with his left hand.

I shut the car off and started walking over.

"Heard you coming all the way up the hill," he said. "Ain't you got a second gear in that thing?"

"I was trying not to get swallowed up by some of those lakes in the road," I said.

"One more thing to get done. At this point, it doesn't make sense to fix the road until spring," he said through breaths as he sawed. "You'd better back up. This branch is about to go."

The limb crashed down into the clearing. Campbell descended the ladder with considerably more grace. We each took hold of a branch and dragged the limb over beside the camp.

"Just leave it here. It needs to season a bit. If I need kindling in the spring, I can come out and saw it up as I need it. If I don't need it, I'll have something to do when the snow melts," he said. "Now. How 'bout a beer? We can sit on the porch and talk."

I walked up the steps, plopped down in a wooden chair, and waited. When Campbell came back, he had two beers in one hand and the two cushions from the fireside chairs in the other. He handed me a beer, the Schaefer bottle opener, and the worst of the two cushions.

"We might be here a while, so I took the thicker cushion," he said.

After he opened his beer, he raised it slightly and nodded my way. I did the same, although I had almost taken a sip of mine before so. Kind of appropriate, this awkward toast, I thought. I wanted to fill the silence by talking about my trip to Milo, but I stopped short. I needed to let Campbell do the talking.

"Over the years, I learned a lot of things about Jim Whyte. As I said yesterday, some of them seemed pretty far-fetched at first, especially his tales about being a pearl diver and things like that, but I came around to thinking he was telling the truth. He got his money from somewhere, after all. But then he went bust. After Tessa left, Lydia Randall started noticing stuff when Jim came to the store. In the old days, if he tore a hole in his shirt, she'd never see him wearing it again. Now he started putting patches on his clothes. Then she heard about him selling that emerald ring—she told me about that when it happened. It was pretty clear Whyte was scraping to get by. Then one afternoon, I was up at his cabin and the truth came out. He'd invested heavily in German shipping businesses before the war and lost every cent."

Campbell took a swig of beer and set the bottle down on the arm of the chair. For a split second, I looked at it. The label was facing toward me. He glanced down, then turned the bottle so the label was properly facing him again.

What is with that habit? I thought. I'd never seen anyone do that before and never would for the rest of my life. I wanted to know but wasn't going to ask. Not now.

"He kept all of his shotguns and rifles and one of his pistols. I think it was a pretty tense time for him. But then things got better and would stay that way up until he died."

I hated to barge in, but I couldn't wait longer. "When did all of this happen again?" I asked.

"After Tessa left. You know, from the time Jim Whyte showed up here with his deed to thirty acres, everybody wanted to know how he made that first pile of money. I'm sure Tom and Lydia Randall told you it was the talk of the store for quite a while. But it quieted down after a few years. At least until the feds showed up in 1917 to see if he was a German spy. That got a whole new round of rumors flying. But the thing was, Whyte wasn't coming down from his cabin all that much, so people finally figured he was telling the G-men the truth. You can't be a spy if you're not talking to anyone. Then, two years later, the Onawa train wreck came along. That made everyone stop thinking about Jim Whyte for a while. Everyone except me, that is."

"Wait a minute. Jim Whyte had something to do with the train wreck?" I asked.

"Sort of," said Campbell. "That's a whole story within a story. We'll need another beer for that."

"I'll do the honors," I said. I was afraid if Campbell went inside to get them, he might get sidetracked. When I got back, I even opened the beer and handed it to him. Anything in the name of getting back to the scene faster. Fortunately, he took a swig and got back on track.

"The day of the wreck, I'd gotten up while it was still dark—easy to do because it was close to the shortest day of the year. It hadn't snowed hard in a while, but it was only a matter of time before it did, so I decided to make my way down to Randall's Store to buy a few things while I had the chance. It was just before I got there that I heard the god-awful screeching of both trains' brakes followed by the crash. Bam!" he said, slapping his hands together to emphasize the impact.

"When I got there, it was a horrible. Almost makes me cry to this day. Some people were moaning inside the wreckage, others were screaming for help, still others were hobbling along next to the tracks in a daze. Both engines and the first car of the passenger train—the luggage car—were demolished. That luggage car was smooshed down like an accordion. It was only one-third its original length. There were suitcases and carpetbags scattered all over the place. Some of them had been tossed forty feet off into the snow. Fire, twisted metal, and screaming—that's what I remember most. It was a terrible scene."

"Were you the first one there?" I asked.

"One of the first. There was one person who got there before me. He was on the other side of the tracks. When I was running from the smashed luggage car back toward the passenger cars to see if I could help anyone, I looked between the cars and saw someone moving away from the train toward the woods. Like I said, the snow wasn't that deep, so he got out of my view pretty quickly. What I couldn't figure out was why he was running in that direction. There wasn't anything to run to. But then I realized who it was—Jim Whyte."

"Jim Whyte was on the train?" I asked. "As a passenger? That seems like quite a coincidence."

"That's what I thought, too, until something happened to make me think different. I climbed up into the first car and stuck my head out the other side in time to see Whyte turn onto the trail up to his cabin. Just as he turned onto the trail, he glanced back toward me and our eyes locked for a second, long enough so he knew it was me and vice versa. I don't know why, but I actually waved at him. He nodded and kept going up his trail.

"I couldn't waste any time thinking about why Whyte was there or what he was doing. I needed to help get people off that train. I went into the first passenger car and tried to get as many people out as I could. It wasn't more than five minutes later when a bunch of folks from town arrived. I remember seeing Dr. Clancy and thanking God he was there to help. We were racing time because those wooden cars could catch fire and we'd all be done for. One by one, we pulled people out of their seats and practically shoved them down the aisle and off the train. People were standing below catching folks and getting them the hell away from the wreckage. At one point, I looked down at the crowd ushering people away. I'll be dammed if one of the people wasn't Jim Whyte. I figured he must have had second thoughts about running home. But, you know, after we saved everyone we could, I looked around again and Jim Whyte was gone. Nobody else from town had left. The injured folks had been taken to Milo, and the passengers who weren't hurt were taken to the church in Monson. The volunteer fire department had the flames under control, and the dozen of us who had been there from the beginning stood in the snow recounting what we'd seen. I almost brought up Jim Whyte, and probably would have if he hadn't come back to help, but he'd done the right thing by pitching in, so I let it go."

Campbell scratched at the corner of his beer label with a fingernail for a moment, then stopped. He took his feet down from the post, put both hands on the arms of his chair, and pushed himself back so he was sitting straight up.

"At that point, Whyte and I were both aware that he had a secret. All he knew for certain was that I'd seen him running away from the wreck. He hadn't met me before that day, and wouldn't for another seven years, but he must have figured I was keeping my mouth shut about seeing him there. And you know, he was right. I didn't even tell your uncle. Sure, I had my suspicions, but I hadn't really seen Jim Whyte do anything that day other than act a little strange. So, life eventually went back to the way it was around here."

Campbell paused for a few seconds, winced, and shook his head once from right to left. "That's not quite right," he said. "Things were never the same for your Uncle Roy or the people who were on that train and their families. But most people got back into their routines. Until the FBI came back, that is."

"They what?"

"Five years after the wreck. It wasn't the same crew that came before. In fact, there were just two of them this time. The bureau must have had a record of where Whyte's cabin was because they didn't stop at Randall's Store for directions like they had before. The way Whyte told it to me, he saw them walking up through the clearing, so he pulled a shotgun off the wall and stepped out onto the porch. They yelled up that they were FBI agents and wanted to ask him some questions."

"They still thought he was a spy?" I asked.

"Oh no. They'd moved on from that. Now they wanted to know if he was up to something else," he said. "They came all the way to Onawa to ask this guy in his mid-sixties if he was running some kind of crime ring. They must have felt silly once they saw old Jim. I imagine the only reason they asked any questions at all after they saw him was that they'd come up here from DC or New York or wherever they came from and they needed to file a report or something."

He leaned back in his chair, put his feet up on the porch post, and took a breath.

"I suppose you wonder how I found out about it. Well, after that first trip to Whyte's cabin—the one I told you about yesterday—I started visiting him more often. Your Uncle Roy was still putting himself through hell because of that train wreck. It wasn't as easy being around him as it used to be. Sometimes we'd spend a whole afternoon fishing, and he'd barely say a word. That was hard, even for a quiet, old loner like me, so one day, I took a walk up to Whyte's. Spending time with him was the opposite. Whyte was a man who'd been quiet for years and had a lot to say, and your uncle was a guy who barely stopped talking for years and suddenly had nothing to say at all."

Campbell looked at me for a reaction. I smiled. I wanted him to know that I didn't take what he was saying about Uncle Roy personally. I also didn't want to say something stupid that would make him stop talking.

"I'd been up there half a dozen times or so before I visited him on a July afternoon. It was the day after the feds visited, as it turned out. I was shocked when Whyte told me they'd been to his cabin. I even wondered if he was pulling my leg, but he swore they had walked up through the field and stood in front of his cabin asking questions until they'd seen and heard enough. Whyte and I sat talking on his porch for a while, like we always did.

"On one of those earlier visits, he talked about the money. He had come into a lot of it in the years after he left home. Most of it came from sailing cargo ships. When he got back to the states, he put a big chunk of cash in a New York City bank. Like I told you yesterday, he swore that settling down, especially in the world's largest city, was the worst choice he could have made. The noise alone drove him crazy. So, he took most of his money out of the bank and set off to find a place to rebuild his life—a place people wouldn't think of looking for him. That place was Onawa."

"So, he was hiding from her family," I said.

"At first he was," said Campbell. "Eventually, there would be more people to hide from, too. But one person he never hid from was his mother. She lived almost her whole life in New York City. It wasn't long after coming to Onawa that Jim got back in touch with her. He made sure she was taken care of the rest of her days. He and Tessa went down to see her from time to time. The last few years were really tough. She started losing her mind, and Jim moved her to an old folks' home—a really good one. When things got really bad, he and Tessa went down to get her and brought her to Monson. She lived into her nineties. I can't remember what year she died, but it wasn't long before Tessa left Jim."

As much as I wanted to say "She's buried in Milo," I kept it to myself. Good thing, because Campbell was in the mood to talk.

"That July night, he asked me if I wanted to try some of his hard cider. I didn't think he drank at all, so I was kind of surprised. I joked about it being a special occasion, and he told me it was, that he'd gotten those FBI guys to go away. We went inside, and he opened a hatch door leading down to his root cellar. He went down there and scurried back up the ladder with a corked jug. 'This batch is pretty strong,' he said. Boy, I guess. One sip of that was enough for me to feel a good glow.

"We went back out onto the porch. I'll never know whether the cider loosened him up, whether he'd thought it through earlier, or both, but what Jim Whyte talked about that night put me on a path I couldn't imagine ever being on."

Campbell stood up, wheeled around, and looked at me. "Ben, I'll be damned if that old man hadn't been trading in opium for years."

"Good God. Smuggling opium from Onawa?" I asked. "How?"

"Remember our deal, Ben," he said. "None of this can be shared with anyone. Not your parents, not Tom and Lydia Randall. Not anyone. At least until after I'm dead."

"I promise, Phil," I said. We'd come this far with the story. I needed to hear the rest, no matter where it led.

"When Jim Whyte was sailing around the world, he made friends in Shanghai and other Chinese ports of call. The opium trade was booming, especially in New York City. There were dozens of opium dens in Chinatown alone. When Whyte was in China on one of his trips, he met a guy named Tommy Lee. They were both about the same age and hit it off. Over the years, Whyte shared stories with Lee about life in America—enough to convince him that things were better here. Well, Tommy Lee not only came to the states, he ended up being one of the most powerful men in Chinatown. He founded a gang called the Leong Tong that controlled most of the opium dens, gambling joints, and whorehouses. Lee made boatloads of money. He took payoffs from the people who ran the illegal businesses, paid the cops to look the other way, and pocketed the difference.

"Over the years, Jim Whyte and Tommy Lee stayed in touch. They didn't send many letters, though. It would be too risky. Instead, Whyte would go to Chinatown when he was in New York, or he'd keep tabs on what was going on by reading the *Police Gazette* and other newspapers. There was a lot of coverage because there were so many killings. At the worst of it, Teddy Roosevelt was named police commissioner, but even he couldn't make it all stop. There was too much money and too much greed."

"So, he became president instead?" I asked.

Campbell got a good laugh out of that one.

"Yes. I imagine he liked that job more, though. Tommy Lee died in 1918. Jim Whyte went down to the city to attend the funeral. There were thousands of people there, and even a brass band played. He met one of Lee's nephews there, who told him if he ever needed money, he knew who to contact."

Campbell had been sitting for too long. He picked up his beer, stood up, and told me to stay put. He stuck one finger into his beer bottle, leaned against the porch post, and kept talking while the beer bottle dangled at his side.

"After a few months went by and Whyte was broke, he made the decision to become a bagman. I wonder if he ever thought about changing his mind on that train ride down there or if he figured there was no turning back. I never asked him, but I'm pretty sure I know the answer. The money was too good not to risk it.

"Tessa was long gone when he set up his operation. He ran his whole part of it by himself. The opium came into Vancouver. The only place between the Pacific and the Atlantic where the train wasn't in Canada was when it went across Maine. Jim Whyte's cabin couldn't have been in a better place. All he had to do was walk down to the tracks, pick up the opium, travel to Chinatown, and make the handoff. The money he made would be sent to William Boscenc, care of the Guilford post office."

"Oh my God," I said. "It's incredible. So, he'd planned on doing this from the time he bought the land?"

"I don't know for sure. I never asked. I figured he was smart enough to buy the land so he'd have options. If I had to guess, I'd say he tried to stay away from a life of crime as long as he could. That was the main thing about Whyte. He never looked the part. I couldn't believe I was sitting on the porch with a man who told me that he ran opium for a living and I still doubted it was true. One thing's for certain—if Tom and Lydia Randall found out that their assistant postmaster was an opium runner, they'd keel over. That's why I never want to drag them into this. They're better off keeping out of it. Everybody is."

I thought about Tom and Lydia Randall. Sometimes it felt as if they were the only thing keeping the town together. Probably because they knew the boundary line between what they needed to know and what they didn't. If they poked too far into anybody's business, they'd lose business. They must have known that whatever Campbell knew was something they wanted no part in.

"The day of the train crash was the day Whyte was going to retrieve his first package of opium. It was supposed to be tossed the night before from the eastbound train, but the brakeman wasn't sure where to throw the stuff, so he didn't. Their backup plan was for the brakeman to throw the package from the caboose on his way back through—in broad daylight, no less. Talk about risky! When the train crashed, the brakeman got thrown off the back of the train and rolled down the embankment. He was lucky there was at least some snow on the ground. He only broke his arm. Whyte ran back, picked up the opium, and got out of there. His plan was to run up to his cabin, but when he saw me, he went partway up the trail, hid the box under a log, and then went back to the wreck so it wouldn't look like he was up to something. After that, they waited several weeks before starting up again. That's when they started signaling and doing the drops only at night."

"Where was Uncle Roy after the collision? Did he see the wreck?" I asked.

"Poor Roy," he said. "They never should have allowed him to get anywhere near that disaster. When we were pulling people off the train, I looked up and he was standing there shaking his head. He was so distraught. Finally, someone convinced him to go back into town. I think they took him to Tom and Lydia's."

"Did you ever tell him about Whyte and the opium?" I asked.

Campbell winced and half turned to look out over the clearing. Wrong question, I thought.

He took a deep breath and turned back toward me. "Roy was such a stubborn bastard. As soon as I told him about Whyte's smuggling, he didn't want anything to do with him—didn't even want to hear his name." Even years later, recounting the story made Campbell shake his head.

"What was I going to do, not tell him about it? He would have been even angrier if I knew Whyte was using the railroad he worked for to smuggle stuff and I never said a word. But he didn't see it that way. We actually got into a quite an argument about it. Roy wanted to report Whyte to his bosses. At least I talked him out of it. 'Jeezus, Roy,' I said. 'You really want to do that? What has the guy ever done to us? The guy's old and broke. Why not just leave him be? He'll never get caught. He's the last person in the world anyone would suspect.'"

"And that's where you left it?" I asked.

"Not really," he said. "Roy was still worried that he might get asked about smuggling rumors one day. He told me that if he got asked, he'd have to tell the truth. He was loyal to that railroad. I understood why, especially after they kept him on the payroll through the worst of times. In the end, Roy decided that if he didn't have any contact with Whyte—including me telling stories about him—he'd be able to say he didn't know anything about him.

"Over the years, all I had to do to make Roy scowl was to mention the name Jim Whyte. Sometimes, like that time you were with us on Borestone, I said the name just to get a rise out of him. He was really mad at me after your parents came to get you. He made me promise not to mention Whyte in front of you again. But your uncle never understood two things. The first was how much he and Jim Whyte were alike. If Roy had ever met him and given it a chance, they really would have gotten along. I always felt it was a shame he dismissed Whyte out of hand. Of course, that was all my fault. The second thing was that when a man doesn't have a job and has no chance of getting one, he's apt to do desperate things. I hoped that one day Roy would understand that, but his mind got filled up with guilt from the train accident instead.

Truth is, Roy never lived a full life after that wreck. If the sun ever broke through the clouds he had around him, it was a good day. It was a good thing I never told him what I'm about to tell you."

Campbell pulled his finger out of the beer bottle, raised the bottle to his mouth, and took the last two gulps. He set the bottle down on the arm of his chair and stepped back to lean against the post again. He shifted around a bit while he looked for something else to hold in his hands. Finally, he defaulted to lifting his shirttails and plunging them into his front pockets.

"That evening on the porch, Whyte asked me if I'd do him a favor," Campbell said. "He said that he might have fooled those FBI guys, enough to make them go away, but he was worried that if he left town on the train, they'd find out he was on it. I said that wouldn't be a problem if he wasn't carrying opium with him. 'That *is* the problem,' Whyte said. 'I need to get out of the business, but I have one last drop to make. Will you do it? There's money in it for you. Lots of money.'

"Before I could say anything, he waved me into the cabin and down the ladder into the root cellar. I'd never seen such a well-stocked larder in my life! He had shelves and shelves of applesauce, peaches, jams, venison, all that he'd canned himself. He moved a few jars of peaches aside, pulled a rock out of the back wall, and took out a small bag of opium from his cache. 'It's one pound,' he said, holding it out toward me. 'I need you take it to Chinatown and drop it off. You'll be done before you know it. I'll give you traveling money. When you get back and we get the money in the mail, I'll give you three hundred bucks. That's everything they'll pay me for the deal. I really need to get this done, Phil. If they don't get the drop, they will come here to get revenge.'"

Campbell shook his head as he recalled the scene. "He said he didn't want me to take the bag then, that he'd keep it hidden until the day I left town. He just stood there waiting for me to say something. I almost started laughing thinking about the absurdity of it all. A well-dressed gentleman in an Onawa root cellar asking me to make an illegal dope run to New York for him."

I could picture Campbell standing in that cellar surrounded by glass jars of meat and fruit wondering what to do.

"Then something more absurd happened. I said yes. But not just for the reasons he gave me," he said. "Sure, the money was part of it. Three hundred dollars would last me quite a while. But more than that, I wanted to keep us both out of trouble. I'd already been involved for years, ever since I saw him at the wreck, which he knew about, and ever since I saw him meeting the train that October night, which he didn't know about."

"Holy cow. You went to Chinatown for him?" I asked.

"Yup. A one-shot deal if there ever was one. When I think back on that night on the porch, it seems like it never happened. The only other person who knew about that conversation until tonight died ten years ago. But we really were there, watching the sunset take shape over this very ridge we're sitting on, with him telling me how to get to Chinatown and what to expect when I got there."

Campbell sat forward in his chair and rubbed his hands together as he started in on the story he'd only shared once in almost twenty years.

"We planned it out pretty well. Whyte came up with the idea of driving me down to Milo and having me catch the Bangor and Aroostook train south. If I left from Onawa, too many people from around here would see me. If he dropped me off in Milo, he said he could pick up his mail from Guilford on the way back. It was part of his regular routine. I ducked down in his car until we got out on the road. There wasn't much traffic between here and Milo back then, so I only ducked down when we saw someone coming from the other way."

Back then, I thought. Try earlier today. I think I saw two cars all the way there and back.

"Of course, nobody would miss my being gone for a few days. I only went to Randall's Store a few times a week and sometimes only once. It was pretty exciting to be taking the train from Portland to New York. That Union Station in Portland is one nice place to wait for the Boston train. Anyway, I made it to New York and to Chinatown in Lower Manhattan. That's when I began to realize that as I walked, I was turning from a tourist into a criminal. From here on out, at least until I made the drop and got out of there, I'd really need to be on my toes. Whyte's description of what to expect helped me there. The opium dens weren't as big a draw in Chinatown as they used to be, so I had to be careful not to look out of place. One problem for me was that it was full of cops. Whyte warned me that after generations of turf wars, the police and the city had finally shut down a lot of the opium dens, card rooms, and whorehouses. Some places had shut down, while others had moved across the river to New Jersey. It wasn't like the streets were empty, but I couldn't meld in as easily as I could have if there were lots of people there. Even though Whyte warned me, it didn't seem dangerous to be running his errand when we were drinking cider and talking about it on his porch. But once I was there, I just wanted to do what he told me to do and get the hell out. The problem was I couldn't do it so fast that I drew attention.

"As I turned onto Mott Street, I felt sick to my stomach, and I felt drops of sweat on the back of my neck. There were cops working both sides of the block. I didn't know if either of them was on the take, and I was hoping I wouldn't need to find out. I got to 18 Mott Street. It was a five-story brick building with a fire escape on the front, just like Whyte described it."

Campbell took a deep breath and closed his eyes. Even all these years later, the scene made him nervous. It was no wonder. He had lived through it and shared the story only once before.

"I walked up to the guy on the steps who was standing guard and said I was there on account of an old friend named Tommy Lee. He didn't say a word. Just took a long look at me. Finally, I said I had come down from Maine. That did the trick. He opened the door a crack, said something, and then the door opened to let me in. Three men led me down a narrow hall, where another door opened into a large card-playing room. There were five tables with games going, and at least another five empty ones. The players and dealers didn't look up, and I didn't look around—not at them, anyway. I was too busy trying to memorize where the windows and doors were in case the place got raided while I was there.

"The guy who was leading the way led me to a door in the back of the card room. He knocked lightly six times, and the door opened. There was a man half my age dressed entirely in black sitting behind a desk."

"Tommy Lee's nephew," I said.

"That's what I figured," said Campbell. "He asked me why I was there. I said I had come down from Maine to run an errand for William Boscene. Lee's nephew asked me where the stuff was, and I said it was in my chest pocket. With that, his henchmen reached in and took out the opium. I guess they didn't want to take a chance that I was going to draw a gun. They unwrapped the package, checked out the contents, and handed me fifty bucks—two twenties and a ten. I was a little surprised because Whyte had said they would be mailing the money to Guilford. Lee's nephew said it was 'traveling money' and that I should take my time leaving Chinatown and buy a few things from stores on my way out, so I'd be less suspicious to the cops. He also told me to spend an hour in the card room, so it would be less obvious I'd made a drop."

"And you sat there like he said?" I asked. "That must have been hell."

"It wasn't that bad. I was better off watching the card games than playing them. I just sat in a corner and waited. I tried to convince myself that it wasn't any worse than a slow day of fishing, but it didn't really work. You don't get killed going fishing too often.

"When I got back out onto the street, I did just what Lee's nephew told me. Good thing—the two cops were still walking their beats, and who knows if there were undercover people around. So, I turned to walk deeper down Mott Street and looked around until I found a fruit stand. It was the only food that looked familiar to me, so I bought some oranges and apples. Looking back on it, that was pretty stupid. Why would I go to Chinatown to buy fruit? But I was lucky. Nobody stopped me on my way out of there."

"So, it wasn't as dangerous as you thought?" I asked.

"Are you kidding? It was ten times more dangerous than I thought. The gang wars got crazy down there. More than forty people were gunned down in the six months after I got back to Monson. Whyte picked a good time to get out of the business. I wouldn't go down there again, even if it was for three hundred and fifty bucks."

"But you did get paid?" I asked.

"Oh, yes. A week after I got back, Whyte had the money for me. He told me to keep the fifty bucks I already got paid as a bonus. I told him I wouldn't ever be a bagman again. He said he wouldn't, either. He told Lee's nephew that he was getting too old to run errands anymore. He sure as hell wasn't going to tell them that the feds were onto him. I suppose if he hadn't been a good friend of Tommy Lee, they might not have let him quit so easily. But he never heard from them again."

"So, you got $300, and $40,000 went to the grave with Jim Whyte," I said. "That's what a few years of smuggling opium did for him."

"Pretty much," said Campbell. "From what I could see, he hardly spent any of it. Just enough to keep him clothed and fed. I think he wanted to leave the money to Tessa. But nobody ever found a will. That first stroke should have been enough to make him want to write one, but the second one kept him from doing it at all. I always felt it was why he was so excited to see me in New Jersey. He wanted me to get the money and track down Tessa."

Campbell pushed his way back into his chair again, took a swig of beer, and let out a long sigh. He didn't say anything for the longest time. I couldn't help feeling that he was thinking about how the stories had ended for Uncle Roy and Jim Whyte and likely wondering why he was the last man alive.

"Jim Whyte was the most interesting man I ever met," he said. "There were two sides to almost every part of him. He knew six languages and barely ever spoke more than one. He traveled the world for half his life and rarely left Onawa for the rest of it. He was outgoing, yet he holed himself up in a cabin. He married at least twice, maybe three times, and he died alone. He made a fortune, lost it, earned another one, then left it where no one would ever find it."

"You left out the part about opium," I said. "What about that? Why did you take the risk? You could have been shot or gone to jail."

"Like I said, I didn't think about any of that until I stepped into Chinatown. I suppose I could have turned around and come home, but all I could think about was doing my job and getting back out. There really wasn't any more to it than that. One thing I knew—Whyte wasn't going to run any more dope after that. He knew it was time to stop. I just helped him do it."

Campbell paused and scratched at the upper right corner of his beer label for a bit. "Whyte's strokes took him by surprise," he said. "He didn't plan to die anywhere other than in his cabin. But God had another ending in mind. Fact is, Ben, it's all a crapshoot. Do we die like Roy, doing what we love? Like Whyte somewhere far from home away from everything we love? No one knows until it happens. The only thing I do know is when my time comes, I pray to God it happens here."

Fading Away

Campbell was sixty-nine years old when he told me about his opium exploits with Jim Whyte. It was another ten years before I could share the story with anyone. By then I'd finally gotten that job as a reporter. In fact, I had just been promoted to become the head feature writer and was spending most of my days racing against deadlines when I got the news that Campbell had died.

Those days I spent in Onawa in the autumn of '46 ended up being more of a gift than I could have imagined. The following winter was the last one Campbell would spend in his cabin on the ridge. By late spring, he began showing signs of mental decline. He was put in a home for the elderly in Monson—the same one Lizzie Whyte had spent her final years in—where he drifted in and out of lucidity for another nine years.

When I heard that Campbell was gone, I decided to take an early lunch break. There was a park next to the Press Herald Building where I often escaped from the newsroom chaos. I took a seat on my favorite metal bench, set the brown paper bag containing my lunch beside me, and looked up at the clouds until I couldn't see them through my tears. Campbell's death had filled me with remorse and regret.

I had known about Phil Campbell's mental decline. In the ten years since we had last talked on his porch, I'd only been able to make it up to Uncle Roy's camp a few times, once by myself, once with Elizabeth just after we were married, once with Mom, and the rest with Elizabeth and the boys when they were still whirling dervishes.

The first trip I took up there was just before I met Elizabeth. It was October of 1948, almost two years to the day since I had last left town bound for Onawa. But this time, I only had three days off.

One thing that had changed was I had a new car. My 1947 Ford was a lot more likely to make it up there and back than my old clunker. I rolled into Monson around noon on Friday, so I stopped to see Tom and Lydia at the store. That was when I first heard about Campbell. It may not have come up at all if I hadn't mentioned going up to his cabin to see him.

"I guess you haven't heard," said Tom. "Last spring, he got taken to Swanson's, the same home where Lizzie Whyte spent her last years."

"Oh my God. What happened?" I asked.

"Tom and I started noticing things," said Lydia. "At first, they weren't a big deal. He'd forget what he came here to buy and such."

"Then one day he stopped in and said he was going to visit Roy," said Tom. "That's when we knew that he couldn't live up there on the ridge by himself anymore."

"So sad," said Lydia. "But he does seem happy at Swanson's."

"If you want to see him while he remembers you, now's the time," said Tom. "He still recognizes us, but we don't know how long we have before he won't."

"I didn't see that coming," I said. "He was always so buttoned-up."

"We didn't, either," said Lydia. "It came on pretty fast."

I thanked Tom and Lydia for filling me in and promised I'd stop back at the store later that weekend.

I pulled my car up Main Street a few blocks, shut off the engine, and sat by the curb to think about Campbell. The easy decision would be to drive to Uncle Roy's and remember Campbell the way he used to be. I wondered what I could gain out of seeing him in a place that compromised his independence. Then I thought about Jim Whyte. If Campbell could take a train ride all the way to New Jersey to visit a friend, how could I not drive half a mile to do the same?

I'd never set foot in Swanson's, but I knew where it was. It was an old Victorian house set one block back from the east side of Main Street right near the church. The joke in town was that when people got old, they made three stops on their way north—first at Swanson's, then the church, and finally, at the graveyard. It was good for a chuckle the first few times I heard it, but it didn't seem so funny now.

I parked the car out front and walked up the five steps onto the porch. It was a splendid fall day, and there were a few old guys sitting in chairs. One was asleep with his chin tucked down onto his chest. The other looked up at me as I was about to open the front door. His eyes widened in recognition.

"Phil Campbell," I said, incredibly relieved that he at least knew I was familiar. "It's Ben. Ben Harmon."

"I know," he said. "Come have a seat."

There were a handful of wicker chairs to his left, and I pulled one up next to him. "It's good to see you. How are you?" I asked.

"Where do I know you from?" he asked.

"I'm Roy Harmon's nephew. We used to go fishing together on Lake Onawa," I said.

"Yes. Roy." He smiled and looked out at the blazing red maple in the yard for a while. "How is he?"

My stomach sank. I turned away from him and looked toward the lawn. I felt my eyes tearing up. I didn't know what to do. It was like when I caught my first fish and I needed Uncle Roy to yell from the porch to set the hook.

Part of me wanted to pull him back to reality. To ask things like whether he remembered Jim Whyte or living in the cabin his father built or even using an old log as an ottoman, but what would that do for Campbell? Would it make him any happier than he was just sitting here in the sun watching leaves drifting down from maples? I decided not. The best thing I could do was just sit here with him being a friend.

"He's doing fine," I said. "He says to say hello."

"We need to go fishing soon," he said.

I pictured the three of us getting ready to set out from the dock on one of those beautiful August days after Campbell had washed off the slate dust and we had hours of fishing ahead of us.

"I'm sure he's waiting for you, Phil," I said.

Elizabeth

Most people who worked at the newspaper ate in the cafeteria on the first floor above the printing press in the basement. I tried to avoid it as much as I could. It was busy and noisy. The newsroom offered enough noise and drama without me having to get another helping of it during lunch. To be sure, I loved the challenge of writing a story and getting it turned in by deadline, even when it meant I couldn't take a break, but when I was finally able to take an hour to recharge, I preferred to take it outside.

Lincoln Park, right next to the office, was my green oasis in the city. Created after most of Portland burned down in the Great Fire of 1866, it was ringed by eighty-year-old maple trees. Each corner of the park had impressive granite columns with (always open) wrought iron gates and sidewalks that led to a beautiful fountain in the center. Unless it was winter, I almost always went to the park to eat the sandwich I had made the night before.

One day while I was sitting on my favorite bench (the one halfway down the quietest side of the park), I was startled to hear a woman's voice pulling me out of a daydream about a story I was working on.

"You're Ben Harmon, aren't you?"

"Yes." She was standing with her back to the sun, and I must have looked goofy squinting up at her. I tossed the second half of my sandwich in my bag and stood up to shake her hand.

"Oh, I'm sorry. No need to get up. I just wanted to say that I enjoy reading your stories. My name is Elizabeth. I just started working in classifieds."

Before the end of my lunch hour, I was smitten. (And not just because she loved my newspaper stories.) I knew she was pretty right away. But it wasn't long before I also learned she was funny, inquisitive, and a great conversationalist. In fact, it seemed like the conversation we started in Lincoln Park just kept flowing. That had never happened between me and anyone. We talked about world events, advertising, movies, baseball, you name it. It wasn't long before lunches in the park were standing dates. Dinners and evenings at the movies weren't far behind. Then came meeting each other's parents. But I saved my stories about Uncle Roy and Onawa for last.

I don't know why I didn't think Elizabeth would enjoy the cabin, but I hesitated to take her there. It wasn't that I thought Uncle Roy wouldn't have approved of her. He would have loved Elizabeth. I think I was more afraid that she could never understand why the place was so important to me.

I needn't have worried.

We went up on a Friday night the August after we were married. On Saturday morning, she asked me to take her out in the canoe to show her the lake and how to cast a fly rod. We paddled down to the end of the lake so I could show her the Onawa Trestle. As we sat in the cove, I started telling her the story of Uncle Roy, Jim Whyte, and Campbell. By the time I was done, we had paddled back to the cabin, cooked dinner over an outdoor fire, and watched the stars come out over Borestone.

Elizabeth was amazed by it all. We had carried Roy's old Adirondack chairs out by the fire ring. I tossed a piece of driftwood on the coals and waited for the flames to flare up. The silence wasn't awkward, just peaceful. I waited for Elizabeth to say something.

"Ben, will you take me to Jim Whyte's cabin?" she asked. "I want to see where Jim Whyte lived." She hesitated a second, then added, "And I want to see that view from the porch."

"That's a question I hadn't expected," I said. "I'm not sure we should go. It's been three years. I don't even know if it's still abandoned. Maybe it's best if I just remember the way it was."

"You said that about Campbell, too," she said. "But you were glad you went."

Man and Nature Stake their Claims

I was afraid to stop at Randall's Store. On the one hand, we'd find out whether someone else owned Jim Whyte's cabin. On the other, we needed to get back to Portland that day. My concern that introducing Elizabeth to Tom and Lydia would lead to too many old stories and we'd never get onto the trail helped us decide to skip the introductions until we had more time. I made coffee, then oatmeal on my backpacking stove so we wouldn't have to wait for the woodstove to warm up.

The dirt road to the trail hadn't changed much. I even joked to Elizabeth that I remembered most of the potholes. What had changed was the trail itself. More people were using it these days. There was room for two cars to park next to it now, and the muddy section at the beginning had a few logs placed over the worst parts so you could walk on them instead of sinking up to your ankles.

When we climbed up to the junction with "the Jim Whyte trail," we met another surprise. It was gone. To be more accurate, it was closed. The sign for the trail had been removed, and the old blue paint blazes on the trees had been covered over with brown paint. To really make sure people didn't take the old route, someone had felled a big spruce tree across the old path.

"Follow me," I said. "I know the way."

As we worked our way around the spruce and back onto the path, I proposed the new plan. "We'll hike this ridge over to Big Wilson Cliffs,

look down on the cabin, and see if anyone's there. Then we can decide
what to do."

On the way to the viewpoint, all the old trail markings had been
removed. The cairns were gone. The blazes on the rocks were painted
out, too.

"My guess is that someone bought the cabin and doesn't want anyone
going over there anymore," I said.

When we stepped out onto Big Wilson Cliffs, Elizabeth said three
words. "Oh my God."

"Indescribable, isn't it?" I asked. "There's Monson. You can see the
church. And over there is the Onawa Trestle." Then, turning back to the
scene below us, I looked down to see another incomprehensible sight—
Jim Whyte's cabin had been burned to the ground.

"Shit." I seldom swore, but it was the first word out of my mouth. I
dropped down, sat with my legs hanging off the cliff, and just stared.
Elizabeth sat down next to me. I thought back to Campbell's description of seeing Dora and Jim Whyte sitting in this very spot, and I put
my arm around her.

"I can't believe it's gone. He built that thing like a tank. Must have
been those vandals again. Can't people just leave things alone?"

"I'm sorry, Ben. So sorry. It was my idea to come up here."

"It's not your fault. I would have found out about it, anyway. I'm just
glad Campbell will never know."

We sat on the rocks for quite a while. I needed to let my thoughts
settle for a bit. It didn't seem right to look at that clearing without
Whyte's cabin in it. It would be like looking across Lake Onawa and not
seeing Borestone. I gazed down again at where his cabin used to be. The
only thing left was a brown square marking where the walls once stood.
I looked up the hill behind the desecrated spot and thought I saw something back at the edge of the woods.

I stood up and grabbed Elizabeth's hand.

"Come on. We need to go down there," I said.

"But there's nothing to see."

"Oh, yes, there is."

We dashed down the old trail toward Jim Whyte's as quickly as we
could without tripping over roots and rocks. When we got to the clearing, I continued past the spot where the cabin was and up into the woods.

"Where are you going?" Elizabeth yelled between breaths from below.

"Just up here. I was right!"

I waved Elizabeth up through the few birch trees on the ridge toward where I was standing. "It's still here!" I exclaimed.

As we both stood trying to catch our breath, Elizabeth was able to get out a few words of disbelief. "An outhouse? We ran down here to look at an outhouse?"

"Not any outhouse. Jim Whyte's."

I was so excited to see some vestige of Jim Whyte. It didn't matter what kind of building it was. "He made this." I took the stick out of the hasp and opened the door. "See, he even wrote something in German on the wall."

Elizabeth still didn't seem impressed. I was closing the door again when she held out her hand.

"Stop!" she said, grabbing the door before it could swing shut. "I know German." She said the words aloud. "*Wir werden zu früh alt und zu spät schlau.* We grow too soon old and too late smart."

"Perfect," I said. "His parting message to us all."

I looked around at the fern-covered ground around us. "Do you believe there's $40,000 buried around here someplace and no one ever found it?" I asked.

"Nope. Because I don't think he ever buried it here," she said.

"Where else could it be?" I asked.

"Well, my first thought was that it was in the mattress on that bed where he traced the numbers with his fingers. But then I thought about it some more. There's no way he would have carried that much cash with him on his way there. And if this whole area was destroyed and nobody found it, then it's not here, either."

"So, of all the places in the world it could be, we've ruled out two," I said.

"It's a start," she said. "To me it just means it will never be found." She pushed her fingers back through her long, brown hair, gathered it in the back, then held it on top of her head. "Phew, I'm hot. Let's take a break."

"I know just the spot," I said.

We walked into the clearing and down past the burnt patch where a piece of exposed ledge created a nice seat for two.

"Well, I can't show you the view from the porch, but this is close," I said. "This is where I set up Uncle Roy's tent that night."

I turned to our left and pointed up at Big Wilson Cliffs, then over to the ridge where Campbell had lived.

"It's beautiful here, Ben. I can see why Jim Whyte wanted to stay."

After we sat for a while, we got up to poke around the cabin's old site. One thing I had missed before was how well the fire had been contained.

"I'm not so sure it was vandals who did this," I said. "If someone had just torched the cabin and run away, you'd think the field or even the woods might have caught fire. Not only that, but whoever did this also filled the old cellar hole first. Probably to get people to stop coming up here to dig."

"So, someone stood here and tended the fire? That must have taken days."

"Not just tending the fire but filling the cellar hole before that. It must have taken a day's work just to throw enough rocks and dirt in there. It also means we can find out who did it. Tom and Lydia Randall will know for sure," I said. "I'm also willing to bet that whoever burned the place down saved Jim Whyte's woodstove, too."

Elizabeth laughed. "What makes Ben Harmon happy? Outhouses and woodstoves."

"Don't forget fly-fishing," I said.

"I think you run quite a bit deeper than that," she said.

"I'm glad you noticed."

I put my arms around her from behind and spun us back toward the view. I looked over toward Campbell's ridge, then turned my gaze southwest. Elizabeth was already looking that way. I knew she would be. Campbell's ridge to our right and the Borestone ridge to our left framed the scene better than any fine artist ever could. Jim Whyte had seen it. So had Dora, Tessa, Fred Hall, Campbell, and even Uncle Roy.

"It sure hurts to see the cabin gone. I thought that thing would out-last all of us. But they can't take away this view. Not yet, anyway."

"Even with almost everything gone, I certainly wouldn't mind com-ing back," she said.

On our way back down to the car, I kept thinking that in a few years there'd be no sign of Whyte's cabin at all. Nature always wanted to take her landscapes back. Whoever burned the cabin down and filled in the cellar hole had given her a head start. The field grasses would come first, then a few pioneering spruce or hemlock trees. By then it would be hard to imagine that anyone ever lived on the ridge above Big Wilson Stream and the railroad tracks. I was sure glad I had the memories of spending time there and the six photos Campbell had given me. They were practi-cally the only things left to show from a remarkable man's life.

Gone Too Soon

I dabbed Dad's forehead with a cool, wet washcloth. The nurse said it might help keep him comfortable. I couldn't believe it had come to this. I thought I'd have more time with him, to fish in front of Uncle Roy's and maybe just talk. But the cancer was going to rob us of that. The only silver lining at all was that he had gotten to meet both of his grandsons.

It wasn't quite his time yet, but he didn't have much. The doctor said he might pass as soon as tomorrow. Elizabeth, Mom, and the kids had gone to Deering Oaks to have a picnic so I could have some time, just him and me.

I dabbed his forehead again and he made a funny face—a bit of a scowl.

"Okay, Dad. No more washcloth," I said.

I found it touching that the man who always had trouble expressing his feelings was now doing it without words.

Our relationship had always had an air of formality to it in both words and actions. Dad always spoke precisely, covering ground he needed to without leaving much room for discussion. Most often, it felt like Dad saw words as tools for getting things done right. Sentences were crafted with the same precision as wooden shelves. He taught me the worth of taking time to choose the best words for the job—the writer's equivalent of measuring twice and cutting once. Now he lay helpless in a hospital bed, no longer able to create an outcome and waiting for the one beyond his control. At only sixty years old, it didn't seem fair.

If he could suddenly open his eyes and talk to me, I wondered if he would say that everything was all right, that he'd been given a forty-year lease on life because he wasn't meant to walk off that battlefield in France. That's what I hoped he'd say.

Dad rested there with his eyes closed all afternoon. He looked like he was taking a nap. Every once in a while, a nurse would come in and ask if he needed a little more morphine. She'd pour a few sips of water in his mouth, tell me to go to the nurse's station if I needed anything, and then go back to her rounds.

About four o'clock, the rest of the family came back from Deering Oaks. Elizabeth was amazing with Roy and Charlie. Roy was five, so he understood a bit more about what was going on than Charlie. When their visit was over, she took the boys home, so it was just Mom, Dad, and me.

Neither one of us had ever sat with someone who was dying. Mom was handling it really well. While we sat, she told stories about what Dad was like when they met at a Deering High dance and first started dating. She talked about how much he loved working at the office supply company even if it wasn't what he'd gone to school to study.

Around ten o'clock, things took a bad turn. Dad's breathing started getting worse. He was taking deep breaths and holding them before finally letting the air out in one big sigh. Mom ran to get the nurses. They gave him one last dose of pain medicine, and we held his hands as he slipped away.

After a pause, one of the nurses walked over to the window and opened it. "To let his spirit out," she said. They asked us to leave the room for a few minutes. When they let us back in, Dad's face had gone completely white. That's when I knew his spirit had indeed gone out the window and into the night.

They put Dad's body on a gurney, draped an American flag over him, and wheeled him out to the hearse for the ride to the funeral home. We formed a little procession, the doctor, the nurses, Mom, and me. Once Dad's body was loaded into the hearse, the staff from the hospital turned and went back to work. Suddenly, as the hearse turned out the driveway, Mom and I were the only ones left standing there, all that remained of Dad's immediate family.

I don't know why, but I looked up. The sky was blanketed in cloud cover. There wasn't a single break in the sea of white. I looked straight above my head just as an opening formed. The clouds parted to reveal a single star.

"There he is, Mom," I said. "He went straight from his hospital bed to heaven."

Return to Uncle Roy's

Mom said it was important for her to go with me to clean Dad's things out of Uncle Roy's cabin. I had offered to do it myself, but she said it would help her adjust to life without Dad.

I tried not to say too much as we went through the few things Dad had left there, clothes and tools mostly. Thankfully, Dad had added to Roy's collection of tools and materials. He was always finding things to patch up like holes in the porch screens, although Mom tried to keep his projects small-scale. "We didn't come up here so I could watch you work," she'd say. "You do enough of that back home."

We'd left Portland early on a Saturday so we could collect everything and get an early start home the following day. When Mom insisted on doing that, I figured her visit was more to say goodbye to the cabin than anything. Now that we were there, it seemed like she had a different opinion.

"Roy built a great cabin," she said. "Has nothing to do with how it was made. We had so many good times here. It always felt good to arrive and sad to leave. I wanted to make sure you'd always have good memories of this place, too. It's good to have a place like this in your life, a place where you can come to think great thoughts or maybe not have to think at all."

She took a break from folding shirts and stacking them on the bed to look around the room.

"It's hard to believe this is the second time I've been here to get someone's things after they passed. Of course, there's not much to take this time. It's not like sorting through Roy's stuff. He lived here. We mostly just visited."

The way Mom was talking, I knew she'd be back here again, hopefully many times, but I wanted to get her word on it.

"It's your cabin now, Mom. You shouldn't stop coming here."

"I came up here with the intention of handing you the keys. I'm still going to," she said. "It's your turn now."

"I figured that's why you wanted to do this so quickly after Dad's service. But I'll only take the keys if you promise to come up here with us a few times a year. Elizabeth and the boys want you to, and I do even more."

She smiled. "Only if you don't make me do it in the winter. It's just too damned cold."

"All right. No winter visits," I said.

That afternoon we went to Randall's Store to get some things to have for dinner. We'd left the cabin at four thirty so we would be sure to make it there before they closed. When we walked in, Lydia came right up to give us both hugs and say how sorry she was to hear of Dad's passing. Her warmth came through as dependably as ever, but during our visit, I noticed that she was moving with a "one task at a time" deliberateness I hadn't seen before. Lydia carefully poured two cups of coffee, set them on the counter and asked Mom to carry them over to the table so they could catch up on things. I stayed at the counter to talk with Tom.

"I'm sorry I didn't stop by the last time I was here, Tom. I wanted to, but we ran out of time. I brought my wife Elizabeth up to show her Uncle Roy's cabin and we ended up squeezing in a hike over to Jim Whyte's before we left. His cabin was burned down."

"It sure was," he said. "A guy from Massachusetts named Hunter bought the property. He decided the cabin wasn't worth saving and needed to be burned down. All sorts of varmints had moved in and done damage—mice and red squirrels, mostly. But the kicker was the roof. Two winters ago, the snow load made it cave in. Once the place was wide open to the elements, it got to the point it would be better to start over."

"Such a shame. It was so well built," I said.

"More than most of us knew. Hunter told me that Whyte had driven ash dowels down through the logs to give the walls extra strength. That meant Hunter and his son had to cut the logs into more pieces. They must have been swearing at Whyte a lot when they tore it down."

"Then they burned it?" I asked.

"Yup. Some of the logs had started to rot and the others were now too short to reuse for anything, so they burned what was left of the roof and the bad logs and stacked the good ones somewhere nearby."

"I'm surprised I didn't see that," I said. "I see they left the outhouse."

"Hunter didn't say much more, but he did say two things. One was that they didn't get anything worth saving from Whyte's cabin other than the woodstove."

"No money," I said.

"Exactly. But Hunter said something really interesting after that. He was so impressed with Whyte's cabin that he took measurements and pictures of it before he tore it down. I'll be damned if he isn't going to build a replica of it in the same clearing."

"Why would he do that?"

"Damned if I know. You'd have to ask him. I don't think he's here this weekend. He usually stops here on his way in. He almost always has his son along with him."

My thoughts switched to someone I knew would still be in town.

"How's Campbell doing? I've been thinking of him a lot lately. Have you seen him?"

"Lydia and I went to see him last week. The poor guy. He's friendly enough. Nods as if he knows who we are even though he has no idea. But he is happy to have visitors."

"I'm glad to hear he's doing well."

"Does that mean you're not going?"

"I'll see how Mom feels in the morning. She may want to get an early start. No promises, but I'll try," I said.

"Just be prepared. He won't have a clue who you are," he said.

A Profound Connection

Mom insisted on making pancakes for breakfast. I wasn't going to argue with that. The only rough part was when I opened the woodstove door to light the fire and we realized that Dad was the one who'd left it ready to light. I handed Mom the box of matches. Of course, the fire was roaring in seconds. We both wiped tears away as the fire crackled below.

"Let's eat on the porch," said Mom. "You can take the butter and syrup out there."

We didn't say much. There was little that hadn't been said about Dad, and the view was just what we needed to regain some peace. The mist rising off Lake Onawa reminded me of the day I caught my first fish on my second cast with a fly rod. The trout were even rising. It was reassuring that nature's rhythm and Uncle Roy's cabin were such constants in my life.

"Why don't you visit your friend Campbell before we go?" asked Mom. "I can clean up the dishes while you're gone, and we can still get an early start back down to Portland. Tom and Lydia will be at church, so we can skip stopping at the store."

I worried a little about leaving Mom alone. Of course, she knew that already.

"Go ahead. It's important. I'll be fine," she said.

I dreaded seeing Campbell all the way to Swanson's. Dad's death was so recent. I didn't know how I'd handle seeing another person whose mind had left his body behind.

There weren't as many people at Swanson's as usual. Those who were able to attend church had been chaperoned there for the service. Campbell was one of the few who had stayed at the home. I stopped at the desk and was pointed down the hall to room six.

The door was ajar, so I pushed it open all the way. Campbell was sitting in a chair by the window looking out at the trees. It made me happy to see that some habits lingered even if we didn't always know why.

Campbell was wearing a new plaid flannel shirt. He looked as handsome and strong as ever. Even though he was sitting down, I could tell that his body hadn't deteriorated nearly as much as his mind. He turned and looked toward me.

"Hello!" he said.

"You have a visitor," I replied.

He just smiled. I knew he had no idea who I was. In fairness, why would he? It had been quite a while between visits.

"I just stopped to see how you were doing," I said.

"I'm doing okay," he said. "Folks here are really nice. Are you here to take me to Randall's Store? I need to pick up some mousetraps and smoked sausage."

Oh, dear god. Even though I had thought I was ready for anything, apparently I wasn't.

"We have to wait for everyone to get back from church, then we can go," I said.

"Then come have a seat."

I sat next to him and looked out the window. For the next ten minutes, he talked about things that would have made sense in years gone by, but not here and now—random thoughts splattered like an impressionist artist's blotches on a canvas.

What am I doing here? I thought. Shouldn't I be back at Uncle Roy's helping Mom? Maybe I should make my move and get back to my car.

Campbell reached out and held my hand. He looked me straight in the eyes as tears poured down his face.

"Oh, Ben," he said. He shook his head back and forth. "Oh, Ben."

Despite what everyone had said, Campbell still had moments of clarity within his grasp. I started crying, too. There was no sugarcoating anything. I knew that he knew how badly it felt to be trapped in a body with hardly any mind left. And how much he wished he could have had it all end in his cabin up on the ridge instead of in this sterile weigh station.

"I'm sorry, Campbell. So damned sorry," I said.

He sat back again. I wiped the tears from my eyes with my shirt-sleeves, stood up, and found a tissue box by his bedside. I wiped the tears from Campbell's face.

"So," he said, "are we going to Randall's Store? I need—"

"Some mousetraps and smoked sausage," I said.

"How did you know?"

"I'm sure someone will take you later," I said, reaching for a tissue of my own. The way he had connected with me so briefly only to be pulled back into his mental hall of mirrors really threw me off. I had always viewed reality as comforting. I was happiest when my thoughts were connected with what was happening around me. Now I was seeing a man for whom reality was terrifying. Perhaps living in a world of confusion and random glimpses of happiness was best.

"I need to go now, Phil. I am really glad I came to see you."

Before I left the room, I turned to look back at Campbell. He was staring out the window again. As long as he had trees and birds to look at, I knew he'd be happy. It would be easy for anyone looking at him to believe that he'd already forgotten I was there. But on at least one level, he did know. He'd looked me in the eyes and said so.

On my way back to my car, I realized that I was still shaken by Campbell's sudden moment of clarity. For a long time, I tried to figure out why he had experienced it with me. But I finally settled on simply being honored that he had.

Some Chapters End. Others Begin.

I drove up to Monson on my own to attend Campbell's funeral. On the way there, I decided to visit Evergreen Cemetery in Milo. No new names had been added to the Mooers family gravestone. I was happy to know that Tessa was still alive and perhaps still in Bangor with her sister-in-law. I said a prayer for both of them before I got back in my car.

The community church in Monson was half filled with parishioners when I arrived for the service. Only a handful more people would show up. It made sense. Almost all of Campbell's contemporaries were already gone. Tom and Lydia Randall were the last to arrive for the service. They were helped down the aisle by two youngsters I didn't recognize—a niece and a nephew, no doubt. The Randalls both looked incredibly frail, especially Lydia. I was seated on the aisle, and Tom squeezed my bicep and winked on his way by.

I'd never been to a service at this church, and judging from the proceedings, Campbell hadn't been, either. It wasn't the pastor's fault, but there was a lot of talk about the general arc of life and death and not much about the man who was lying in the coffin.

The scene made me think of something Campbell had said when we first met—"Each life is a story that only lives as long as the people still alive to tell it."

I began to realize that when Tom and Lydia Randall passed, the stories of Uncle Roy, Campbell, the Onawa train wreck, and Jim Whyte would all be buried with them. That was too much history to let slip away forever.

After the service, Tom and Lydia invited me for coffee. I wasn't going to turn them down. There were lots of people there, most I didn't recognize. The way things used to be are always being replaced by the way things are, I thought. I made a special effort to see Lydia and Tom. We couldn't talk much. There was too much noise, and I could tell they were tired. All I really wanted them to know was how good it felt to see them again. We held hands in greeting and smiled.

There were other people waiting to say hello and I didn't want to tire the Randalls out, so I started saying that I should go. Tom wasn't having it. He raised his right hand and pointed toward the porch. "I'll meet you outside," he said.

As I stood on the deck looking out over Lake Hebron, I thought of the day we sat out here and first talked about Jim Whyte. I heard the door opening, and Tom walked out.

"It's good to see you, Ben. I'm really glad you came up here for Campbell's service. He would be happy," he said.

"To be honest, Tom, I'm happy, too. Happy you encouraged me to see him that last time. It was one of the best things I could have done for both of us," I said. "And a great way to remember him."

"They say we never know how much time we have to enjoy things, but it's even harder when we're still here and we can't remember them," he said. "That's why I wanted to make sure I gave you something before you left town."

Tom pulled his hand from behind his back and handed me Jim Whyte's brass telescope. "Some things need to be passed along," he said. "It will mean more to you than anyone else."

I didn't know what to say other than "Thank you." I was suddenly aware that this might be the last time I'd ever see Tom Randall alive. I wanted to say more, but it took me so long to say it that he turned back to go inside.

"Wait," I said. "I don't have any gifts for you, but I want to thank you and Lydia for everything you did for Uncle Roy and Campbell...especially Campbell."

Tom turned around and took a few steps my way. "Why especially Campbell?" he asked.

"Because you knew he had a secret, and you never pushed him to find out what it was," I said.

"Oh, that," he said. "You mean Campbell's opium run to New York?"

"You knew?"

"Not for a few years. Jim Whyte told us one day. He was long since out of the business, and he and Campbell were both in the clear. I was furious at first. But Whyte convinced me that no money ever came through the Monson post office and the only money that ever came north was to a different name, so that Lydia and I couldn't get into trouble," he said.

"And you never told Campbell?" I asked.

"What was the point? It was better to let it go and act dumb. It's a small town, Ben. Nothing stays secret for long unless you know who you can trust your secrets with. Even though it was by accident, I had let Campbell down once and he held a healthy grudge about it for a long time. It wasn't worth firing up another one. I didn't know how smart I was to make that decision until he stopped remembering who I was. I would have felt terrible if we hadn't parted friends."

"I'm glad we did," I said. I wondered if I should have told Tom about Campbell's moment of clarity but thought better of it. There was no sense in reframing the story for Tom only to lead him to a worse ending.

Through the window, I could see Lydia waving Tom in toward the party. I waved to Lydia, shook Tom's hand, and said, "Goodbye." He held my hand for a beat longer than normal and looked me in the eye.

"I'm glad we met, Ben," he said.

"It would be hard to imagine this town without you," I said.

When I left Tom and Lydia, I drove into Monson to use the pay phone in front of the store. The old hand-painted "Randall's Store" sign that used to hang in front of the door had been taken down. A new sign, stretched across the entire front of the building, said "Morrill's Market" in large block type and had Coca-Cola logos on both ends of it. Another little piece of the town's personality had been taken away. In time, I wondered whether there'd be anyone who remembered or cared about Monson's history at all.

I stuck a dime in the coin slot and called home to Elizabeth. I wondered if she'd be willing to watch Roy and Charlie until Sunday night. I had some writing to do.

Epilogue: A Lingering Reminder

In the 1950s, extremely high floodwaters beached a twenty-four-foot powerboat on the northeast shore of Lake Onawa. The boat was stranded so far inland that the lake's waters would never reach it again. By 1963, most of the derelict boat was in rough shape. The bottom had completely rotted away, but the sides were still holding on. If you stood behind the boat in the afternoon light, you could just make out the faded letters of the boat's name gracing the stern: *Tessa*.

Jim Whyte and his Maine Coon cat pose on the cabin porch in 1905.
Photo courtesy of Richard Shaw.

Onawa Trestle as it appeared during Jim Whyte's time. Built in 1896, it replaced the original 1887 wooden trestle. Photo courtesy of Monson Historical Society.

Canadian Pacific Railroad tracks and Borestone Mountain (date unknown). Photo courtesy of Monson Historical Society.

Jim Whyte (in white driver's cap), Judd Lord and Whyte's dog show off Whyte's 1910 Apperson town car, believed to be the first private automobile owned north of Maine's largest city, Portland. Photo courtesy of Monson Historical Society.

Village at Monson, Maine

Postcard view of Monson as it would have appeared during Jim Whyte's time (specific date unknown). Photo courtesy of Monson Historical Society.

Jim Whyte (foreground) and Tessa at the cabin in 1914. Photo courtesy of Richard Shaw.

Jim Whyte (center) and friends at the cabin in 1924. Note the woodpile taking shape for the winter. Photo courtesy of Richard Shaw.

Author's Notes

The place names used in this book are largely accurate. Some locations, such as Phil Campbell's camp, have been invented. As stated
in the story, Jim Whyte's cabin no longer exists. It was burned down by
a subsequent landowner because it had fallen into disrepair.

Tessa Mooers Whyte lived until just short of her ninetieth birthday.
She died in 1962 and is buried in the family plot in Milo, Maine.

The stories about Jim Whyte tickling a deer's ear and tossing pancakes through the skylight came from published accounts. Did they
really happen or are they tall tales? We'll likely never know.

Places don't stay beautiful unless everyone pitches in to keep
them so. If you go to Monson, Onawa, Milo, or other locations mentioned in this book, please respect the land and the landowners.

Sources

Articles

"About 'Jim' Whyte." *Piscataquis Observer* (Dover-Foxcroft, ME), January 25, 1934.

Ende, Albion. "Jim Whyte, Hermit of Little Wilson." *The Moosehead Gazette* (Greenville, ME), July 11, 1969.

Johnson, Stanley E. "Folks & Incidents I Remember at Onawa." *Piscataquis Observer* (Dover-Foxcroft, ME), March 14, 21, and 28, 1963.

Sawyer, Roland J., Jr. "The Mystery of Jim Whyte and his Woodland Lookout." *Boston Sunday Herald* (Boston, MA), January 7, 1934.

Shaw, Dick. "The Mysterious Jim Whyte of Elliotsville, ME." *The Moosehead Gazette* (Greenville, ME), April 4, 1975.

Books

Douglas, Paul H. *In the Fullness of Time.* New York: Harcourt Brace Jovanovich, 1972.

Seligman, Scott D. *Tong Wars: The Untold Story of Vice, Money and Murder in New York's Chinatown.* New York: Viking, 2016.

About the Author

Jeffrey H. Ryan is an author, adventurer, photographer, and historian. He has written several books about his outdoor exploits, his fascination with hiking trails, and the people and places found just off the beaten path. His debut book, *Appalachian Odyssey: A 28-Year Hike on America's Trail* was hailed by the former executive editor of *National Geographic* as "a classic of nature and travel writing" and set off a national tour (in a 1985 VW camper, no less). When Jeff isn't trekking, chasing down a great story, or spinning yarns from his keyboard, he enjoys sharing his adventures with audiences who love the outdoors. He spends much of his time in his beloved native state of Maine. Learn more at JeffRyanAuthor.com.